FAUST

Opera in Four Acts

Music by

Charles-François Gounod

Libretto by
MICHEL CARRE
and
JULES BARBIER
After the poem by Goethe

English Version by
RUTH and THOMAS MARTIN

ED. 2679

G. SCHIRMER, INC.
New York

46104cx

Note

G. SCHIRMER, INC.
609 Fifth Avenue
New York 17, N. Y.

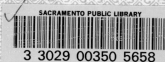

FAUST

Breathe the name of Faust and Devil-smoke may curl from a neighbor's ear, so universal has become the legend of the man who sold his spirit to the powers of evil. Yet Faust is a modern addition to the age-old story of black magic, to the tale immemorial of the outcast who has gone at witching hour to a crossroads and there, standing within a burning circle traced by his own staff, called Satan to his aid. Across the centuries, Mediterranean lands and their races have been less responsive to this type of magic than the gloomier tribes to the North. Italy has produced no famous wizards; practitioners of magic in Spain were gypsies, rather than natives; and even Gothic France felt no vogue for the supernatural. The adepts at black magic flourished in Germany, the British Isles, Scandinavia, the Slavic countries, and that seventeenth-century haven for witches, Massachusetts.

Into this caldron of the ages stepped Faust — a man who actually lived in Germany between 1480 and 1540. Some confusion exists about his Christian name, recorded variously as Georg and Johann,[1] impelling historians not long ago to the belief that two Hell-bent individuals, bearing the identical surname, must have flourished at the same time. Modern research has reduced them to one, the name varying with the places visited.

One thing is certain: despite all possible ambiguities, Faust made a definite impact on the people of his time. An unscrupulous and thoroughly immoral fortune-teller, teacher and wizard, he attended the University of Heidelberg (B.A., 1509) and studied divinity at Wittenberg. "But," as an old English account put it, soon after his demise, "Faustus being of a naughty minde and otherwise addicted, applied not his studies, but took himself to other exercises". Charged with gross misconduct while teaching in a boys' school at Kreuznach (a document of the time refers to him as "the great necromancer and sodomite"), he beat a retreat in order to escape the law, refused a safe conduct to Nuremberg in 1532, and boasted continually of his prowess in the magic arts, referring to the Devil as his brother-in-law, and offering — for a sum — to reveal the future. At one point, he predicted that a colonial expedition bound for Venezuela in 1540 would meet with failure, and he was proved to be right. Ultimately, the man is said to have met a frightful death.

For the most part, Faust was a notorious character whose suspected links to Satan overshadowed any real attainments in his lifetime. Stories about his sins proliferated. He was alleged, for example, to have raised the ghost of Helen of Troy and cohabited with her. This feat, combined with other tales of the supernatural, inflamed the German public and gave quick rise to Faust's universal association with the damned. Almost immediately after his death, he became the hero of a literary tract — the *Faustbuch* — by Johann Spies (the book was published at Frankfurt-am-Main in 1587), describing his pact with the Devil. There followed a second *Faustbuch,* this one by Georg Rudolf Widmann; and confusion was heightened for a time through the popular association of Johann Fust, co-inventor of printing, with the infernal Johann Faust.

The *Faust* cult soon spread to England. Spies' book was translated almost at once by a British scholar with the cryptic pen-name of "P. F., Gent."; and shortly

[1] Goethe, in the epic play which took this man's pact with the Devil as its point of departure, changed his name to Heinrich.

thereafter, inspired by this translation, appeared the celebrated play of Christopher Marlowe: *The Tragicall History of Dr. Faustus.* Back went the expanded subject to Germany, transformed — through the genius of Marlowe — into an evolving part of the Teutonic *Faust* tradition. Supposedly, the play was given in Frankfurt during the 1590's. Historic performance dates exist at Graz in 1608 and Dresden, 1626.

Marlowe, in this magnificent fresco of a play (modern scholars are not agreed as to the reconstruction of all its details), incorporated the raising of Helen of Troy — "Was this the face that launch'd a thousand ships?" — invested Mephistopheles with a certain impish humor (notably in the Roman episode when Faust and the Devil, disguised as cardinals, give the Pope a hard time); but most importantly, from the standpoint of this tale's evolution into the great morality play by Goethe, Faust is pictured as one who — through virtue and knowledge — at one time helped whole cities escape the plague.[2] Ennui, restlessness of soul have led him into sin.

Basic, in the development of this tale, is Faust's preoccupation with a Classical past. Strong hints of Grecian learnings (so prominent in the second part of Goethe's play) are already marked in the tragedy by Marlowe. Not only does the magician, aided by Mephistopheles, raise the ghost of Helen. He also brings to earth — though fleetingly — the spirits of Alexander the Great and the hero's paramour.

In the Marlowe play, as in all older versions of the legend, Faust is irrevocably damned. Though repentant at the end and praying to the Lord, he is snatched away by the Devil. The Satanic high command appears divided: Lucifer appearing briefly, is the top-level fiend; Beelzebub, his chief lieutenant; and Mephistopheles, a trusted subordinate. By the time this story reached the Romantic era, Mephistopheles alone would hold sway.

The *Faust* tale, enormously popular in the German theater of the 1600's, fell subject to many different treatments, some of them crossed with the comic traditions of Harlequin. All sorts of variations on the original theme took over. It was not, however, until the end of the eighteenth century that the crowning idea of Faust's redemption was advanced. The philosopher-playwright, Gotthold Lessing, is credited as having been the first great name associated with the salvation of Faust. He left, as part of an uncompleted manuscript, a scheme pointing toward the magician's reconciliation with God — a project developed to the fullest by Johann Wolfgang von Goethe (1749-1832).

Goethe's *Faust* is more a weighing of life itself than a theatrical absolute. In Part I of the drama — published in 1808 — the German master lay stress on the emotional element in his hero's career, embodied by the maiden Margarethe (Gretchen): sinned against, corrupted, and yet redeemed. Then in Part II, written years later and completed shortly before Goethe's death, he shifted emphasis to Faust's relations with the world, his attempt to fit into the scheme of universal being, and his final escape from evil through dedication to the welfare of his fellow humans.[3] . . . As in the play by Marlowe, Helen of Troy appears . . . but here the mating of Faust and Helen takes on the symbolic quality of a union between the Europe of a later day and the golden clarity of ancient Greece. Their child Euphorion, like Icarus before him, tries to rise above the earth and, flying too high, perishes.

[2] In the play by Goethe (Part I), mention is made by grateful townspeople of the part played by Faust's father in a similar emergency.

[3] In the memorable epilogue to Part II, one of the monuments of world drama, Margarethe is seen as a Penitent, interceding for Faust at the gates of Heaven.

It has been said that Goethe, in the character of this youth born through the mating of different eras and doomed to an early end, meant to personify the poet Byron.

Although since the time of Goethe the *Faust* legend has moved chiefly in the musical arena, it has also been continued in literature by Adelbert von Chamisso, Christian Grabbe, Nikolaus Lenau (these latter two combining the old story with that of another arch-delinquent, Don Juan), Heinrich Heine . . . and, more recently, Paul Valéry and Thomas Mann. A tale of which the essence is Man and the Devil should be able to keep indefinitely gathering new shapes, forms and variations in every corner of narrative art.

The first of many operas on the *Faust* story — by Ludwig Spohr, produced in 1818 — drew not upon the Goethe play but on sixteenth-century sources. A success in its time, the work has long since disappeared, yielding ground to more vital treatments of the legend. Two other famous operas of the period, though not handling the *Faust* subject, made strong use of an associated theme. Karl Maria von Weber's *Der Freischütz* (1820), a fascinating piece of theater magic concerned with forests, the hunt, and sorcery, centered its plot about an infernal wraith named Samiel, in reality the Archfiend; and Giacomo Meyerbeer's *Robert le Diable* (1831) forged for the first time the now traditional bond between bassos and diabolical rôles (the leading tenor in this opera, Robert, ranks only as a half-devil . . . whereas his basso father, Bertram, is the genuine article). But the source for modern satanic repertoire in general and of the *Faust* story in particular remains the play by Goethe.

The master himself loved music; and in tribute to Mozart, whose works he adored, he contrived a sequel to *The Magic Flute*. As for an opera on *Faust*, Goethe declared that only the great Wolfgang Amadeus might have come close to an ideal setting of the play. Composers of the nineteenth century did not much interest him — strangely, for a man whose most celebrated drama transcended in concept all limitations of time and place. . . . And yet distinguished musicians of the age were linked to the play, even if not by Goethe. Beethoven is said to have been approached by the publishers, Breitkopf and Härtel, with a commission for incidental music in the manner of his score for *Egmont*, but nothing came of the project. When it was suggested to Meyerbeer that he turn his hand to setting Part I of the drama, the noted composer replied: "*Faust* is the Ark of the Convenant, a sanctuary not to be approached with profane music". Among the more exotic might-have-beens was a plan, which came to naught, for an operatic *Faust* with libretto by Alexandre Dumas and music by Rossini. A wilder mating of talents would be hard to imagine.

As the age of program music developed in the concert hall, so did the idea of *Faust* grow in appeal to symphonically-minded composers. By now Goethe's Gretchen had become an inseparable part of the tale, and she was to prevail in two of the more famous orchestral treatments. Thus Richard Wagner, as one of his earliest — and finest — works devised *A Faust Overture,* in essence a symphonic poem, alternating and contrasting two principal themes: the turbulent Faust and the idealized Gretchen. Franz Liszt was later to build an entire symphony on this subject, with a unique three-movement construction: the opening Allegro — tense, somber and troubled — evoking a portrait of Faust; the Andante, a lovely, introspective sketch of Margarethe; and the finale, a satanic parody by Mephistopheles on both preceding movements — since the Devil, "the Spirit who denies", can have no positive identity of his own. At its climax, the symphony passes to a tender reprise of the Gretchen motive as solo tenor and male chorus sing the closing words of *Faust,* Part II:

"The eternal feminine leads us on". . . . Two enormous canvases for chorus and orchestra, also based on the Goethe play, were provided by Robert Schumann in his *Scenes from Faust,* and Gustav Mahler in the second portion of his Symphony No. 8 ("Symphony of a Thousand"). Both Schumann and Mahler have set the mystical epilogue to music with strikingly different but innately moving results.

In the borderland between opera and concert lies the famous cantata by Berlioz, *The Damnation of Faust.* Although following in most respects Part I of Goethe's play, it casts aside one deep-seated concept of the drama: the hero is not saved, but damned. Aside from this notable departure (for which Berlioz pleads a reversion to Marlowe), *The Damnation* offers perhaps the most consistent synthesis in music of Goethe's masterpiece. It is definitely *not* an opera, even though brought on stage many years after Berlioz's death by a well-meaning but misguided adapter (Raoul Gunsbourg — Monte Carlo, 1893). The work — a concert piece — remains episodic, subjective, "interior" in every respect, with the visual elements best left, as the composer intended, to the imagination of the listener.

Opera itself has brought us (skipping a dozen or more forgotten works on this subject) the highly successful *Faust* (1859) of Gounod; Boito's *Mefistofele* (1868, revised 1875), including scenes from both parts of the vast drama by Goethe, with Gretchen (here named Margherita) and Helen of Troy as the dual heroines; and Busoni's *Doktor Faust* (posthumous, 1925), a strongly individual approach to the legend, which has been gathering fame in the past few years. As a bit of interesting by-play, the characters of Faust and Mephistopheles appear in Prokofieff's opera *The Flaming Angel* (1919), set in Germany at the time of the original legend. Although the pair comes into sight only briefly, it is clear — by the end of the work — that Mephistopheles has motivated the whole gruesome cycle of events. For modern tastes, Boito and Busoni may evoke a more exciting and sulphurous quality than the kindly Gounod; but as a favorite with audiences, an indestructible commodity, *Faust* continues to hold the palm.

It is quite unlikely that among the host of composers, both operatic and symphonic, drawn to the Faust legend any could have been less inclined by nature toward the diabolical than Charles-François Gounod (1818-1893). He was an amiable, placid person, of a family devoted to the arts. Gounod's father, a painter, had placed second in the Grand Prix de Rome during his youth and later in life was entrusted with restoring certain of the canvases in the Louvre. The mother was musical. In addition to the artistic flair absorbed from both his parents, Gounod also carried within him a strong religious bent which, after his student days in Paris and a time in Rome as winner of the Grand Prix, led in the direction of church music. On returning to France from his Roman studies, he became organist and choirmaster at the Missions Étrangères, also pursuing a course in theology. The span of 1845-'50 has been described as his years of silence, so immersed did he become in matters of religion.

It took the great Pauline Viardot-García, one of the leading singers of Europe, to bring him out of his shell. This extraordinary artist who had created the part of Fidès in Meyerbeer's *Le Prophète,* held the friendship of Berlioz and many other eminent composers, was the confidante of top figures in the literary world, and commanded enormous respect at the Paris Opéra, reacted with interest when the young Gounod was brought to play his music for her. In 1851 it was she who appeared in his first stage work, *Sapho,* launched in grandeur at the big opera house. From then on, Gounod's career in the theater — though not an overnight success — was assured.

In the following year this composer, responding to his great love for sacred music, became conductor of the Orphéon choral society in Paris, a post which he held for eight years. Yet the pursuit of conducting did not stay his hand at composition. In 1854 he brought off *La Nonne Sanglante,* an unsuccessful work, at the Paris Opéra. Four years later he was engaged by the Théâtre-Lyrique — a forward-looking junior opera house — to compose music for *Faust,* with text by Jules Barbier and Michel Carré.

This was an assignment of which Gounod long had dreamed. His proposed idea on the subject had previously been turned down by Alphonse Royer, director of the Imperial Academy of Music, because: "Cela manquait de pompe".[4] And so he fell in eagerly with the venture planned for the Théâtre-Lyrique. While Gounod was at work on the score of *Faust,* word came suddenly via the Paris theatrical grapevine that a new dramatic version of the tale by a playwright named d'Ennery was to be mounted at the Théâtre de la Porte Saint Martin. Fearing an unnecessary and perhaps ruinous competition, Léon Carvalho, director of the Théâtre-Lyrique, persuaded Gounod and his collaborators to suspend work on *Faust* and turn their attention, for the moment, to another project. After a week, according to his Memoirs, of agitation and soul-searching, the composer agreed and started work on a musical adaptation of Molière's comedy, *Le Médècin Malgré Lui,* successfully produced that same year.

The new play by d'Ennery at Porte Saint Martin met with less acclaim than had been expected. At last it folded its tents, and the Théâtre-Lyrique was ready to proceed with *Faust*. When the score had moved to completion, rehearsals went all ways but smoothly. Whole scenes were suppressed, on demand of the management. The usually amiable Gounod was up in arms about cuts . . . but they were made.

A thoroughly distinguished audience was on hand for the opera's opening night, March 19, 1859. Auber, Berlioz, Delacroix, Pasdeloup, Heugel were among the many leaders of the arts in attendance. Reaction in general proved good but not ecstatic. Berlioz, in his capacity as music critic, wrote in the *Journal des Débats* of "the great and legitimate success obtained by Gounod". He liked especially the simplicity of Marguerite's entrance in the Kermesse; the lovely line of Faust's aria, "Salut, demeure"; and, above all, the poetic ending of the garden scene, with Marguerite's rapturous "Il m'aime!" The performance itself varied in quality. Marie Miolan-Carvalho, wife of the theater's director, sang Marguerite and pleased the public greatly. Until that evening she had been heard only in comic opera, and three years before the première of *Faust* had drawn this unflattering review: "A thin, shrill soprano, as slender as her person, cut in two by three or four pasty notes, a regular bird-pipe". Mme. Carvalho evidently made progress, in the face of this notice, to the point where she was equipped to fill a demanding rôle, for her Marguerite was distinctly a success. As for the tenor, Gounod had set his heart on the engagement of a personable lyric artist named Guardi, who developed vocal troubles in rehearsal, had to withdraw, and left the management looking for another tenor who might quickly learn the part. For a time Gounod himself, possessor of a small but serviceable voice, considered taking over the rôle; but at last Joseph Barbot, a tenor of middle years, teaching at the Conservatoire, stepped in and filled the gap.

[4] "That's not showy enough."

The other principals in this performance were on the adequate rather than brilliant side.

Despite such inequalities of fortune, *Faust* began to build a public. In its early days at the Théâtre-Lyrique, pages of spoken dialogue linked the musical numbers; but for a production of 1860 in Strasbourg, Gounod turned the work into a formal grand opera by replacing all dialogue with sung recitatives. The French musicologist, Paul Landormy, speculates that the so-called "new" version of Strasbourg might indeed have followed Gounod's original plan, since long before Carvalho's invitation to the Théâtre-Lyrique, the composer had dreamed of placing his score at the Opéra, where absence of spoken dialogue was *de rigueur*.

A strange history follows. Owing to theatrical intrigues of various sorts, *Faust* was not performed in Paris from 1859 to 1862. The Théâtre-Lyrique had failed, its doors were closed. Both the new score and its well known Marguerite, Mme. Carvalho, were barred from the stage of the rival Opéra-Comique. An unexpected stroke of good luck, however, retrieved Gounod's fortunes. During the opera's first year, its authors had gone looking for a publisher. It was not easy to find one until Antoine de Choudens, then a beginner in the business, offered his entire capital of 10,000 francs for the rights. In addition, he arranged for performances of *Faust* throughout Germany, where it had a marked success. Returning to Paris, the work proceeded in triumph to a Théâtre-Lyrique newly reorganized by Carvalho. Choudens, in full justice, was to reap a fortune.

At last, in 1869, came the call for which Gounod had waited. Foreign acclaim had touched his opera not only in Germany, where Munich and Stuttgart received it with acclaim, but in Belgium, England,[5] Italy and America.[6] Now a famous international property, its presence was requested on the stage of the Paris Opéra. Through the previous addition of recitatives for the Strasbourg production of 1860, all was formally in order for its presentation in the big house. Only one item was lacking: a full-scale ballet, of which Paris Opéra audiences were traditionally fond. And so a dance episode was added (Act IV, Scenes 1-3), dipping ambivalently into both the Walpurgisnacht of the original play's Part I, with its witchlike fury, and the shining Classical Sabbath of Part II. To offset Faust's distress at dour medieval demons, Mephistopheles causes the famous courtesans of history (including Cleopatra) to appear before him; and here, as a prima ballerina, materializes Helen of Troy: agile, glittering and silent in her white *tutu*.

The remodeled *Faust* traveled first to the old opera house on Rue Pelletier, in use during the Second Empire; and then, with the opening in the early 1870's of the lavish new theater built by Garnier, it became a fixture of the Parisian musical stage, a synonym for all that was melodious and dazzling in lyric drama. Full of recognizable tunes from one end to the other, devilish in its plot without requiring any sense of audience identification, turned out with a fine sense of vocal effectiveness (great singers of the time loved it), and above all never taxing the esthetic responses of a public that wanted to be entertained, *Faust* soon bestrode the Western World. It is said that Queen Victoria adored the work, and one can understand why. On the opening night of New York's Metropolitan Opera House

[5] During this opera's second season in the British capital, Gounod introduced a new aria for baritone, "Avant de quitter ces lieux", in tribute to the singing of Sir Charles Santley, who had created the rôle of Valentin in London one year previously.

[6] Launched on a multilingual toboggan, *Faust* had been introduced to New York (November, 1863) in Italian and, later that same month, to Philadelphia in German.

— October 22, 1883 — *Faust* was chosen as the inaugural score. Christine Nilsson, who had created Marguerite in the Paris Opéra version, was on hand to bring authenticity (although the work was sung, on this occasion, in Italian). Restored, with the passing of years, to its original French, *Faust* became a vehicle for the greatest of Metropolitan singers: Emma Eames, Nellie Melba, Lillian Nordica, Geraldine Farrar, Elisabeth Rethberg prominent among the Marguerites; Jean de Reszke and Enrico Caruso as historic Fausts; Lawrence Tibbett and John Charles Thomas as Valentin; Édouard de Reszke, Pol Plançon, and Feodor Chaliapin as notable interpreters of Mephistopheles. Over a span of forty years — dating from that gala first night until the decade after World War I — no opera may be said to have enjoyed more solid audience popularity. Then the falling away began. The melodies so full of charm impressed a younger generation as cloying. Gounod's sense of the dramatic — especially in the diabolical sequences — was found to lack bite. Perhaps at the root of it all lay the disappearance of the supple, aristocratic vocal style asociated with earlier New York performances. In any event, *Faust* — though still on the list of favorite operas — lost ground in audience affection. During the last season in the old house (1965-'66), the Metropolitan revived the score as a sentimental gesture, with a backward look to the opening night of 1883. Public response was loyal but not overwhelming.

In Germany and Austria, where the work still attracts, it is billed invariably as *Margarethe,* as if to imply that this imported opera must not be confused with a national treasure: the Goethe spoken play. For the guardians of the Ark, Gounod's approach is lopsided. In dwelling on romantic aspects, he has stripped the drama of its philosophic point. But for judges less harsh, the Gretchen element, set to music with so much sensitivity, provides survival power. Long after Mephistopheles has strutted his final exit and Faust carolled his attractive tunes, it is the deeply felt, movingly sympathetic treatment of the heroine that comes through in a great performance. The ending of the garden episode, so justly hailed by Berlioz; the Church Scene in which Marguerite, tormented by the Devil, intones a prayer that soars above orchestra, chorus and organ; and the girl's madness that precedes the closing trio . . . all these, with the presence of a first-class Marguerite, can evoke for us some of the fervor that must have been experienced by audiences of a former day.

That Gounod was definitely not a single-shot composer is shown by the success, following *Faust,* of his *Mireille* (created by Marie Miolan-Carvalho at the Théâtre Lyrique in 1864 and now a staple of the Paris Opéra-Comique) and *Roméo et Juliette* (1867), currently in the repertoire of many of the world's leading opera houses.

NOTES ON PERFORMANCE

There are, considering the length of *Faust,* remarkably few cuts; and most of them — such as the deletion of certain pages for chorus in the Kermesse scene — have tended to be restored in modern performance. One passage so seldom heard as to have remained practically unknown returned in the Metropolitan Opera revival of 1965-'66, when Marguerite's aria at the spinning wheel — after she has been deserted by Faust — aroused a cordial interest. Only the answering cavatina sung by Siébel in this same tableau (which precedes the Church Scene) is still omitted.

As for the ballet, it provides the one note of glitter in an opera known otherwise for its scenic sobriety. More often than not, since this chapter has little relation dramatically to the rest of the work, it is omitted . . . but *Faust* loses thereby in visual contrast. It has been darkly alleged, wihout any documentation to prove the rumor, that not Gounod but Delibes provided the additional ballet music of 1869. Whatever the truth — apparently weighted in favor of Gounod — the sequence is academic in sound, frankly in the mood of a *divertissement*. When, as sometimes happens in modern production, expressionistic dance is grafted onto this slight and stylized musical base, an imbalance can result. *Faust* may best be served by presenting the work for what it is: a winsome period piece, conventional in design, touching in sentiment. For the deeper aspects of Goethe's play, one must turn to other adaptations.

ROBERT LAWRENCE

CAST OF CHARACTERS

FAUST	Tenor
MÉPHISTOPHÉLÈS	Bass
VALENTIN, Marguerite's brother	Baritone
WAGNER, a student	Baritone
MARGUERITE	Soprano
SIEBEL, a youth	Soprano
MARTHE SCHWERLEIN	Contralto or Mezzo-Soprano

Soldiers, Students, Villagers, Dancers, Demons

PLACE: A village in Germany

TIME: Sixteenth century

Index

Faust.

English Version by
RUTH and THOMAS MARTIN

CH. GOUNOD.

Introduction.

Fl., Ob., etc.
cresc.
m.s.
Ped.
molto
f
ff
dim.
p
Harp
rit.
a tempo
Fl., Cl., etc.
espress.

cresc.
cresc.
dim.
cresc.
dim.
rit.
a tempo
Horn
p
Ped.
Clar.
Ob.
Fl.
Ped.
Ped.
Ped.
Ob.
Viol.
Largo.
pp
pp

Act I.

SCENE 1

Nº 1. Scene and Chorus.

It is night. Faust, alone, is seated at a table covered with books and parchments; an open book lies before him. His lamp is nearly extinguished.

F.
ture et le Cré-a-teur; Pas u-ne voix ne glisse à mon o-reil-le Un
long vig-ils through the night.— I hear no voice, no word of con-so-la-tion, I
fp
fp
Bn.
Più lento
mot—con-so-la-teur!——— J'ai lan-gui, triste et so-li-
see — no ray of light.——— I have yearned, lone-ly and de-
Vlns.
dim.
p
tai-re, J'ai lan-gui, triste et so-li-tai-re, Sans pou-voir bri-
spair-ing, I have yearned, lone-ly and de-spair-ing, Pow-er-less to
cresc.
f
ser — le li-en Qui m'at-tache en-core à la ter-re! Je ne vois
sev - er the chain That is bind-ing me to the liv-ing. I see no
3
dim.
p
Bn.
f
f
rien! je ne sais rien! rien! rien!
truth, I see no light. No! No!
3
Cl. & Bn.
Horns & Cl.
Vla.
f
f
dim.
p
p
pp

46104

Allegretto. (♩. = 84)
(He closes the book and rises; day begins to dawn.)
Vlns.
pp
Ob. solo
Fl.
Ob.
Fl.
Ob.
Ob.
Fl.
Andante.
Faust.
Le ciel pâ - lit; — de - vant l'au - be nou - vel - le La som - bre
The sky grows pale, — Soon the sun will be ris - ing, An - oth - er
pp
despairingly
nuit s'é - va - nou - it!.. — Encore un jour! en - core un jour qui
night fad - ing a - way! — An - oth - er day, — An - oth - er hope - less
cresc.
fp
fp
dim.

F.
luit!.. Ô mort! quand vien-dras-tu m'a-bri-ter sous ton
day! O Death! When will you come And re-lease me from my
p
f
Allegro. (picking up a flask from the table)
F.
ai - le? Eh bien! puis-que la mort me
bond - age? Well then! If you a-void my
ff
ff
F.
fuit, Pour-quoi n'i-rais-je pas vers el - le?..
path, Why should I not go forth to meet you?
ff
Wind
ff
ff
(He pours the content of the flask into a goblet.)
F.
Andante maestoso.
F.
Sa - lut! ô mon der-nier ma-
To you, last of my days on
Ob., Cl., etc.
ff
p

tin! Sa-lut! ô mon der-nier ma-tin! J'ar-
earth, To you I bid my last fare-well! I
f dim. p poco più mosso
ri- ve sans ter-reur Au ter- -me du-vo-
face with-out a fear The end- -ing of my
ya- -ge; Et je suis, a-vec ce breu-va-ge, Le seul
jour- -ney, For this draft will make me the mas-ter Of my
f
maî-tre de mon des-tin! Je suis, je suis, a-vec ce breu-
des-ti-ny here on earth. This draft, this draft will make me the
(As he raises the goblet to his lips, the voices of women singing are heard outside.)
va-ge, Le seul maî-tre de mon des-tin!
mas-ter Of my des-ti-ny here on earth.
Brass
ff

Chorus (off-stage)
Allegretto. (♩. = 84)
SOPRANOS.
dim.
f
Ah!
Ah!
Vlns.
Wind
dim.
p
Fl., Cl. & Bn.
p
Pa - res - seu - se fil - le Qui sommeille en - cor!
Still a - sleep and dream - ing, Naugh - ty la - zy girl?
Clar. & Bn.
pp
Dé - jà le jour bril - le Sous son man - teau d'or; Dé -
See the morn - ing gleam - ing, Bathed in ros - y pearl. The
Ob.
Cl. & Bn.
jà l'oi - seau chan - te Ses fol - les chan - sons; L'au - be ca - res -
sky - larks are voic - ing Their song all the while, Har - vest fields re -
Fl.
Cl.
Fl.
Cl.
Fl.

san - te Sou - rit ___ aux mois - sons; Le ruisseau mur - mu - re,
joic - ing In dawn's _ gold - en smile. Near the brook and bow - er
Cl.
Fl.
pp
La fleur s'ouvre au jour, ___ Tou - te la ___ na - tu - re S'é - veille à ___ l'a -
Coos the tur - tle dove, ___ Ev - 'ry bud - ding flow - er A - wak - en -
Vlns.
Fl. & Cl.
mour! ___ Tou - te la ___ na - tu - re S'é - veille à l'a - mour! ___
love, ___ Ev - 'ry bud - ding flow - er A - wak - ens to love. ___
pp
Ob. solo
p
Faust.
Vains é - chos de la joie ___ hu - mai - ne, Pas - sez, ___ pas -
Emp - ty ech - oes of world - ly pleas - ure, A - way ___ -
Fl.
sez vo - tre che - min! .. ___ Pas - sez, ___ pas -
way! Go far a - way! ___ A - way, ___ a -
Ob.
pp
ppp

Andante. (He raises the goblet again.)
F.
sez! —
way! —
Ô cou-pe des a-ïeux, qui tant de fois fus
My last and on-ly hope, O gob-let of my
Trombones, etc.
f
fp
plei-ne, Pour-quoi trem-bles-tu dans ma main? Pour-quoi —
fa-thers, What fear makes you trem-ble in my hand? What fear —
fp
fp
cresc.
Allegretto. (♩. = 84)
— trem-bles-tu dans ma main? —
— makes you trem-ble in my hand? —
Ob., Cl. & Bn.
Vlns.
f
f
p
TENORS (The voices of men on their way to work are heard outside.)
Chorus.
p
Aux champs l'au-ro-re nous rap-pel-le, — On voit à
We go to reap in field and mead-ow, — While high a-
BASSES.
p
Aux champs l'au-ro-re nous rap-pel-le, — On voit à
We go to reap in field and mead-ow, — While high a-

peine l'hi-ron-del - le, Qui vole et plon-ge d'un coup d'aî -
bove we see the swal - low Ascend to heights no eye can fol -
peine l'hi-ron-del - le, Qui vole et plon-ge d'un coup d'aî -
bove we see the swal - low Ascend to heights no eye can fol -
le Dans la pro-fon-deur du ciel bleu! Le temps est
low, Lost in end-less heav-ens of blue! The day is
le Dans la pro-fon-deur du ciel bleu! Le temps est
low, Lost in end-less heav-ens of blue! The day is
p
beau! la ter-re est bel - le! Aux champs l'au - ro - re nous rap -
fair, the earth is smil - ing, We go to reap in field and
beau! la ter-re est bel - le! Aux champs l'au - ro - re nous rap -
fair, the earth is smil - ing, We go to reap in field and
pel - le, Le temps est beau, la ter-re est bel - le!
mead - ow. The day is fair, the earth is smil - ing,
pel - le, Le temps est beau, la ter-re est bel - le!
mead - ow. The day is fair, the earth is smil - ing,

Bé - ni soit Dieu! Bé - ni soit Dieu!
Praise be to God! Praise be to God!
Bé - ni soit Dieu! Bé - ni soit Dieu!
Praise be to God! Praise be to God!
Faust.
F.
Dieu!
God!
SOPRANOS.
pp
Bé -
Praise
Bé - ni soit
Praise be to
Dieu!
God!
pp
Bé -
Praise
pp
Wind
pp
Strgs.
Adagio.
F.
Dieu!
God!
f
Dieu!
God!
ni soit
be to
Dieu!
God!
ni soit
be to
Dieu!
God!
Adagio.
Wind
Strgs.
Tutti
pp

Nº 2. Duet.

Allegro agitato. (♩ = 130)
Faust.
Recit.
F.
Vns.
Vla.
Piano.
ff
Mais ce Dieu, que peut-il pour moi?..
But this God, what can he do for me?
Me ren-dra-t-il l'a-mour, la jeu-nes-se et la foi?
Can he re-store my youth and its pas-sion And my faith?
Andante maestoso.
fp
Mau-di-tes soyez-vous, ô vo-luptés humai-nes!
A curse on all the joys, The lust for hu-man pleas-ure,
Mau-di-tes soient les chaînes Qui me font ramper i-ci-bas! Mau-dit
Ac-curs-ed be the fet-ters Chain-ing me so firm-ly to life! Be ac-
soit tout ce qui nous leur-re, Vain es-poir qui passe a-vec
cursed what man finds al-lur-ing, Emp-ty hopes, so brief-ly en-

l'heu-re, Rê-ves d'a-mour ou de com-bats;_ Mau-dit soit le bon-
dur-ing, Fan-cies of love, glo-ry and strife;_ Hu-man hap-pi-ness,
fp
heur! maudi-tes, la sci-en-ce, La pri-ère et la foi! Mau-di-te sois-
too! Ac-curs-ed be sci-ence, faith in God And in pray'r! A curse on them
fp
f
tu,_ pa-ti-en-ce! À moi, Satan!_ à moi!_
all!_ Hear me, Sa-tan, on you I call!_ Ap-pear!_
Wind
f
ff
Moderato. (♩= 80)
Mephistopheles (appearing suddenly)
Me voi-ci!_ D'où vient ta sur-
I am here!_ Is that so sur-
8
Fl. & Vlns.
fff
dim.
p
pri-se? Ne suis-je pas mis à ta
pris-ing? Or does my ap-pear-ance dis-
Andante
p

Me.
gui-se? L'é-pée au cô-té, la plume au chapeau, L'escar-cel-le
please you? A sword at my side, A purse full of gold, On my cap-a
Fl.
un poco animato
Bn.
plei-ne, un ri-che manteau sur l'é-pau-le; en som-me, Un vrai gentil-
feath-er, The el-egant cloak I am wear-ing, I fan-cy, it's ver-y be-
cresc.
f
Poco Meno mosso
hom- -me! Eh
com- -ing! I
Vlns.
f
colla voce
p
bien! doc-teur, que me veux-tu? Vo-yons; par-le!.. Te fais-je
ask you, Sir, what do you want? Speak up, Doc-tor! Are you a-
p
cresc.
f
p
Poco più mosso
Faust.
Mephistopheles.
Faust.
Me.
F.
peur? Non. Dou-tes-tu de ma puis-san-ce? Peut-
fraid? No. Are you doubt-ful of my pow-er? I
Vln.
f
p
Vcl.

Mephistopheles.
Faust.
F.
Me.
ê - tre! Mets-la donc à l'é-preu - ve!.. Va t'en!
may be. I am will-ing to prove it. A-way!
Ob.
Tempo Io poco riten.
Mephisto.
Fi! c'est là ta re-con-nais-san-ce!
Shame! So this is the way you thank me?
Fa.
Vla.
Vla. & Vcl.
Ap-prends de moi qu'a-vec Sa-
You ought to know, with such as
Vln.
tan L'on en doit u-ser d'au-tre sor-te, Et qu'il n'é-tait
me You can-not be-have im-po-lite-ly, Nor be thought-less
pas be-soin De l'ap-pe-ler de si loin Pour le mettre en-
as you are, Call-ing Sa-tan from a-far On-ly to dis-

Me.
F.
Faust.
suite — à — la por - te!
miss — him — so light - ly!
Allegro.
Et que peux-
Are you all
colla voce
Vlns.
f
F.
tu pour moi?
pow-er - ful?
Mephistopheles.
Moderato.
Me.
Tout,.. tout... — mais dis-moi d'abord Ce que tu
Yes, — yes . . . — But first I must know What you de-
F.
Poco animato.
Que fe-rai-je de la ri-
What on earth would I do with
Me.
veux; est - ce de l'or? —
sire. Could it be gold? —
F.
ches-se?
rich - es?
Me.
Bon, je vois où le bât te bles-
Ah, I think that I know what ails

Faust.
Meph.
Me.
F.
se! Tu veux la gloi - re? Plus en-cor! La puis-
you. You long for glo - ry? More than that. Then for
cresc.
Faust.
san - ce? Non! je veux un tré-sor Qui les con-tient
pow - er? No! The treas-ure I want Would in-clude them
Moderato.
Allegro ben marcato. (♩.= 100)
tous!.. je veux la jeu - nes - se!
all! I yearn to be young-a-gain.
Brass
Ob.
A moi les plai - sirs, Les jeu - nes maî-
Oh give me a - gain a maid - en's ca-
dim.
Vln.
tres - ses! A moi leurs ca-res - ses, A moi leurs dé-
res - ses, The youth - ful ex - ces - ses, Ec - stat - ic, di-

F.
sirs! À moi l'é-ner-gi-e Des ins-tincts puis-
vine! Oh give me the glow-ing flame of youth-ful
cresc.
sants, Et la folle or-gi-e Du cœur et des
fire, That pas-sion-ate yearn-ing For love and de-
sens! Ar-den-te jeu-nes-se, À moi tes dé-
sire! The youth and the ar-dor, The pain and the
p
cresc.
sirs, A moi ton i-vres-se, À moi tes plai-
bliss, The joy of the lov-er, The thrill of a
f
sirs, À moi ton i-vres-se, À moi tes plai-
kiss, The joy of the lov-er, The pain and the
rit.
colla voce

Mephistopheles.
a tempo
F.
Me.
sirs! Fort bien! fort bien! fort bien! fort bien! Je
bliss. I see! I see! I see! I see! My
Fl. & Vln.
a tempo p
Vcl.
Poco meno mosso
Me.
puis con-ten-ter ton ca-pri - ce, Je puis con-ten-
com-ing to you is pro-pi - tious, Be-cause I can
p
poco rit.
a tempo
Faust.
Me.
F.
ter ton ca-pri - ce. Et que te don-ne-
grat-i-fy your wish - es. And what price do I
Fl., Clar. etc.
a tempo
sfz
poco rit.
p
Meph.
F.
Me.
rai je en re-tour? Pres - que rien: pres - que
pay in re-turn? Al - most none, al - most
pp
Andante
Me.
rien: I - ci, je suis à ton ser-vi -
none: On earth I am at your dis-pos -
Fl.
Wind
p
f

Poco animato.
Faust.
Me.
F.
ce, Mais là - bas, tu se - ras au mien! Là-bas?..
al, But down there you be - long to me! Down there?
Tp.
p
Mephistopheles.
(holding out a parchment)
Là - bas! al - lons,
Down there! De - cide!
f
p
cresc.
si - gne! Eh quoi! ta main trem - ble!
Hur - ry! What's this? You are trem - bling?
Moderato.
Que faut-il pour te dé - ci - der? La jeu-nes - se t'ap -
How much more do you ask of me? Here is what you are
ff rit.
pel - le; Ô - se la re - gar -
crav - ing! Glow - ing be - fore your
Vlns.
ff

Andante. (♩= 54)
(He makes a sign; a vision appears show-ing Marguerite at her spinning wheel.)
Me.
F.
der!
eyes.
Faust.
Ô merveil-le!
How en-chant-ing!
Hp.
Vlns.
dim.
pp
Vlns. & Harp
pp una corda
marcato il canto
Mephistopheles.
Me.
Eh bien!...
And now,
que t'en
are you
sem- -ble?
will- -ing?
(eagerly reaching for the parchment)
Faust.
Mephistopheles.
F.
Me.
3
Don-ne!...
Quick-ly!
Allons donc!
Well at last!
(Faust signs the parchment.)

Mephistopheles (picks up the goblet from the table.)
Me.
Et maintenant, Maître, c'est moi qui te convie À vider cette coupe, où fume en bouillonnant Non plus la mort, non plus le poison, mais la vie
Now it is I, Master, It's I who will invite you to drain this goblet, Whose effervescent foam No longer holds the poison of death But a life of joy.
(taking the goblet and addressing the vision of Marguerite.)
Faust.
Me. F.
Fl.
À
To
Ped.

F.
toi!
you!
à
To
Ped.
F.
toi,
you!
à toi,
To you!
Ped.
F.
fan-tôme a-do-rable et char-
Oh vi-sion of youth and of
Ped.
F.
mant!
love!
(Faust drains the goblet, and is transformed into a young man.)
Harp
Ped.
(The vision vanishes.)
Wind

Allegro ben marcato.
Faust.
F.
Je la re-ver-rai? Quand? C'est bien!
You'll lead me to her? When? To-day!
Mephistopheles.
Me.
Viens!
Come!
Sans dou-te. Au-jour-d'hui.
For cer-tain! Right a-way.
Allegro ben marcato. (♩. = 100)
Vlns.
fff
pp
cresc.
f
En rou-te!
We jour-ney!
En rou-te! En rou-te!
We jour-ney! We jour-ney!
À moi les plai-
No more shall I
À
No
Vlns.
f

F.
sirs, — Les jeu - nes maî - tres - ses! À moi — leurs ca -
pine — For maid - ens' ca - ress - es, The youth - - ful ex -
Me.
toi — les plai - sirs, — Les jeu - nes maî - tres - ses! —
more — shall you pine — For maid - ens' ca - ress - es, —
F.
res - ses, À moi — leurs dé - sirs! — À moi — l'é - ner -
cess - es, Ec - stat - ic, di - vine! — Once more — the de -
Me.
— À toi leurs ca - res - ses, À toi leurs dé - sirs! — A
— The youth-ful ex - cess - es, Ec - stat - ic, di - vine! — Once
F.
gi - e Des instincts puis - sants, — Et la folle or -
lir - ious flame of pas - sion's fire, — And all the en -
Me.
toi — l'é - ner - gi - e Des instincts puis - sants, —
more — the de - lir - ious flame of pas - sion's fire, —

F.
gi - e Du cœur et des sens! Ar - den - te jeu -
chant - ment of love and de - sire. The fe - ver - ish
Me.
Et la folle or - gi - e Du cœur et des sens!
And all the en - chant - ment of love and de - sire.
dim
p
F.
nes - se, A moi tes dé - sirs, À moi ton i -
ar - dor, The pain and the bliss, The joy of the
Me.
À toi la jeu - nes - se, À toi ses dé - sirs,
The fe - ver - ish ar - dor, The pain and the bliss,
cresc.
F.
vres - se, À moi tes plai - sirs, À moi ton i -
lov - er, The pas - sion-ate kiss, The joy of the
Me.
À toi son i - vresse, À toi ses plai - sirs, À toi son i -
The joy of the lov - er's pas - sion-ate kiss, The joy of the
f

a tempo
F.
vres - se, À moi tes plai-sirs! À moi
lov - er, The joy and the bliss. Once more
Me.
vres - se, À toi ses plai-sirs! À
lov - er, The joy and the bliss. Once
a tempo
sempre f
colla voce
f
— ton i-vresse, À moi tes plai-sirs, À
— the ca-ress, The pain and the bliss, The
toi son i-vres - se, À toi ses plai-sirs, À
more the ca-ress - es, The pain and the bliss, The
moi ton i - vres - se, À moi,
joy of the lov - er, The joy,
toi son i - vres - se, À toi,
joy of the lov - er, The joy,
ff
Ped.
Ped.

Animato.
F.
à moi tes plai - sirs!
The joy and the bliss!
Me.
à toi ses plai - sirs!
The joy and the bliss!
sempre f
(They rush off. The curtain falls.)

No 3. Grand Chorus.

The Fair. (Kermesse.)

At one of the city gates, at the left an inn with a sign showing the wine god Bacchus.

SCENE 2

ver - re Soit plein! Sans ver - go - gne, Coup sur-
beer or be it wine, Strong or mel - low, we don't
Wagner.
W.
Jeune a - dep - te Du ton -
When the wine - jug goes a -
coup, Un - i - vro - gne Boit tout!
mind, For we drink an - y kind.
Bn.
p
stacc.
W.
neau, N'en ex - cep - te Que l'eau! Que ta gloi - re, Tes a -
round, We can al - ways be found! On - ly wa - ter we dis -
Fl., etc
W.
mours, Soient de boi - re Tou - jours!
dain, Drink - ing keeps us sound and sane!
BASSES I (Students).
Jeune a - dep - te Du ton -
When the wine - jug goes a -

neau, N'en ex - cep - te Que l'eau! Que ta - gloi - re, Tes a -
round, We can - al - ways be - found! On - ly - wa - ter we - dis -
mours, Soient de boi - re Tou - jours!
dain, Drink - ing keeps us sound and sane!
Horn
Valve - horn
BASSES II (Soldiers).
Fil - les ou for - te - res - ses, C'est tout
Wom - en, for - ti - fi - ca - tions, We at -
Bn. Basses etc.
un, mor - bleu! Vieux burgs, jeu - nes maî - tres - ses, Sont pour
tack them all! Cas - tles or young - maid - ens, Both are

nous un jeu! Ce-lui qui sait s'y-pren-dre, Sans trop-
bound to fall. And as for the fe-male gen-der, They are-
ff
p
de-fa-çon, Les o-blige à se ren-dre En pa-yant ran-
eas-y-prey, We in-duce them to-sur-ren-der For-a-ran-som
f
çon! En pa-yant ran-çon!
pay, For-a-ran-som pay!
Valve-horn
Horn
TENORS I. (Burghers).
pp
Aux jours de di-manche et de fê-te, J'aime à par-ler guerre et combats;
Sun-day is my one day of lei-sure, When I en-joy gos-sip of war,
Vlns.

Tan-dis que les peu-ples là-bas Se cas-sent la
I'm too old to fight an-y more, I want qui-et
tê-te. Je vais m'asseoir sur les cô-teaux Qui sont voi-sins de la ri-
pleas-ure. I love to sit un-der the sky, Watch-ing the shin-ing riv-er
viè-re, Et je vois pas-ser les ba-teaux En vi-dant mon
flow-ing And the pret-ty boats pass-ing by, See them com-ing and
ver-re! Je vais m'as-seoir sur les cô-teaux
go-ing! I love to sit un-der the sky,
m.s.
Qui sont voi-sins de la ri-viè-re, Et je vois pas-
Watch-ing the shin-ing riv-er flow-ing And the pret-ty

ser les bateaux En vi - dant mon - ver - re!
boats pass-ing by, See them — com-ing and go - ing!
f
SOPRANOS I (Young Girls).
Vo-yez ces har-dis com-pè - - - - -
See these hand-some boys ad - mir - - - - -
Vlns.
p
res, Qui vien-nent là-bas; Ne soyons pas trop sé - vè - - -
ing As we hur - ry by. Let us not be too re - tir - - -
- - - res, Re - tar-dons le pas, Re - tar-dons le
- - - ing, Let's — not be too shy, Let's — not be too

pas, Re - tar - dons le pas!
shy, Let's not be too shy!
Fl.
TENORS II (Young Students).
Ob.
Vo - yez ces mi - nes gail - lar - - - - - - - des
They are look - ing so flir - ta - - - - - - tious,
Et ces airs vain - queurs! A - mis, so - yons sur nos gar - - - - - - - - des, Te - nons bien nos
What a sau - cy air! But if they are too au - da - - - - - - - - cious Then we must be -
cœurs, Te - nons bien nos cœurs, Te - nons bien nos
ware, Then we must be - ware, Then we must be -

SOPRANOS II (Matrons).
cœurs! Vo-yez a-près ces Don-
ware! They would like to make us
Fl.
zel - - - - les Cou-rir ces mes-sieurs! Nous som-mes aus-si bien
jeal - - - - ous Bra-zen wom-an-kind, They don't e-ven have to
qu'el - - - - - - les, Si non beau-coup
tell us What they have in
mieux, Si non beau-coup mieux, Si non beau - coup
mind, What they have in mind, What they have in

Chorus.
SOPRANOS I.
On vou - drait plai - re, Mais c'est en vain!
These hand-some fel - lows Will look our way!
SOPRANOS II.
mieux! Vous vou - lez plai - re, On le sait bien!
mind! Those bra - zen fel - lows Won't look your way,
TENORS I.
Al - lons, voi - sin!
And now I say,
TENORS II.
De cette af - fai - re Vo - yons la fin!
They seem to tell us To look their way.
BASSES I.
Vi - ve le vin! vi - ve le vin!
Drink ev - 'ry day! Drink ev - 'ry day!
BASSES II.
Vi - ve la guer - re!
Here's to the sol - dier!
On vou - drait plai - re,
Are they too cal - lous?
Vous vou - lez
They are too
Al -
And
De cette af -
Come, all you
Vi - ve le vin!
Drink ev - 'ry day!
Vi - ve la guer - re! Vi - ve la
Here's to the sol - dier! Here's to the
cresc.
cresc.

Mais c'est en vain, oui, c'est en vain! C'est en
Oh no, not they! Oh no, not they! No, not
plai-re, On le sait bien, On le sait bien!
cal-lous, That's all I say. That's all I say.
lons! Al-lons, voi-sin! Vi-dons un
now, And now I say, Let's drink our
fai-re Vo-yons la fin, Vo-yons la
fel-lows, What do you say? What do you
Vi-ve le vin! Vi-ve le vin!
Drink while you may! Drink while you may!
guer-re! la guer-re! la guer-re!
sol-dier, the sol-dier, the sol-dier!
ff
vain! C'est en vain, en vain, en vain, en vain, en
they! No, not they! Oh no, not they! Oh no, not
Le mot est fin! Le mot est fin! Le mot est
That's all I say. That's all I say. That's all I
ver-re de vin, Vi-dons un ver-re de
trou-bles a-way! Let's drink our trou-bles a-
fin, Vo-yons la fin, Vo-yons la fin, Vo-yons la
say? What do you say? What do you say? What do you
le vin! le
To-day! To-
Mé-tier di-vin! Mé-tier di-
His life is gay! His life is

vain, C'est en vain, C'est en vain, C'est en vain, C'est en
they! No, not they, no, not they, no, not they, no, not
fin, Le mot est fin, Le mot est fin, Le mot est fin, Le mot est
say. That's all I say. That's all I say That's all I say. That's all I
vin! Al - lons, voi - sin! Al - lons, voi-
way! What do you say? What do you
fin! Vo - yons la fin! Vo - yons la
say? What do you say? What do you
vin! Vi - ve le
day, Day af - ter
vin! Mé - tier di - vin! Mé - tier di-
gay! Hur - ray! Hur - ray! Hur - ray! Hur-
vain!
they!
(to the young girls)
fin! Vous vou - lez leur plai - re, Nous le sa-vons
say. You don't need to tell us What you have in
sin!
say?
fin!
say?
vin! Vin ou bière, Bière ou
day! Fill your glass - es, fill your
vin! Pas de beau-té fiè - re, Nous sa-vons leur
ray! All the pret - ty lass - es Love a hand-some

(to the older women)
De vo - tre co - lè - re Nous ne crai - gnons
You are on - ly jeal - ous, But we do not
bien!
mind,
Vi - dons, vi - dons un ver - re de
Let's leave our cares and trou - bles be -
Vo - yez leur co - lè - re, Vo - yez leur main -
Oth - ers will be jeal - ous But we do not
vin, Que mon ver - re Soit
stein, Be it beer or be it
plai - re, Nous sa - vons leur plaire En un tour de
sol - dier, Oth - ers will be jeal - ous, We do not
rien!
mind!
So - yez sans ver - go - gne, Comme ils sont sans
Flirt - ing with those fel - lows, We are not so
vin!
hind.
tien!
mind,
plein! Sans ver - go - gne, Coup sur
wine. Strong or mel - low, we don't
main! Al - lons en be - so - gne, Sans peur ni ver -
mind. We know how to woo them, Gal - lant - ly pur -

Front qui se ren-fro - gne Rou-git, voi-là tout!
You don't need to tell — us For we know your kind!
goût.
blind.
Il faut être i -
But it does not
Ma fem - me — gro - gne Sur tout.
My wife — will — nag, — but I don't mind.
Leur front se ren-frogne, El - les ont du goût!
We know how to choose For we are not blind.
coup, Un — i - vro - gne — Boit — tout! Jeune a -
mind, For — we — drink — an - y — kind. When the —
go - gne, À l'as - saut par - tout, À l'as - saut par - tout!
sue them, For we know their kind, For we know their kind.
pp
Un ga - lant m'ac - cep - te,
You go on and chat - ter,
nep - te,
mat - ter
Je le dis tout
And we say it
Ga - geons qu'on m'ac - cep - te
That's an eas - y mat - ter,
dep - te Du ton - neau, N'en ex -
wine - jug goes a - round We can —
De ce grand pré - cep - te Fier sol -
When we sol - diers meet them, Quick - ly

Je le prends au mot...
We are not so proud.
haut, Pour se fai - re
loud, We are so much
Tou
I
Dès le pre-mier mot, Dès le pre-mier mot!
They are not so proud, They are not so proud.
cep - te Que l'eau! Que ta
al - ways be found. On - ly
dat n'ex - cep - te Fem-me ni châ-teau; Et cou-
we de - feat them, They are not so proud. When the
Cer-tes l'on doit croi - re
All you do is chat - ter,
gloi - re De tel-les a-
bet - ter Than your com-mon
jours il faut l'en croi - re, l'en croi - re, l'en
know my wife will nag me And scold if she
gloi - re, Tes a - mours, Soient de
wa - ter we dis - dain, Drink - ing
vert de gloi - re, Chan - te la vic -
drums are roll - ing And the trum - pets

À vos beaux dis - cours!
What a jeal - ous crowd.
mours! Il faut être i -
crowd. But it does not
croi - - - - - re!
finds out.
boi - - re Tou - - jours! Jeune a -
keeps us sound and sane! When the
toire Au bruit des tam - - bours!
blow, We at - tract a crowd.
Un ga - lant m'ac - cep - te,
You go on and chat - ter,
nep - te, Je le dis tout
mat - ter, And we say it
Ga - geons qu'on m'ac - cep - te
That's an eas - y mat - ter,
dep - te Du ton - neau. N'en ex -
wine - jug goes a - round We can
De ce grand pré - cep - te Fier sol -
When we sol - diers meet them, Quick - ly

Je le prends au mot!..
We are not so proud.
haut, Pour se fai - re
loud, We are so much
Ma fem - me
My wife will
Dès le pre - mier mot! Fille au bras d'i -
They are not so proud. That's an eas - y
cep - te Que l'eau, Que ta
al - ways be found. On - ly
dat n'ex - cep - te Fem - me ni châ - teau;
we de - feat them, They are not so proud.
Cer - tes l'on doit croi - re
All you do is chat - ter,
gloi - re De tel - les a -
bet - ter Than your com - mon
gro - gne, gro - gne sur tout, il faut l'en
nag me if she finds out, my wife will
voi - re, Voi - là mes a - mours, Oui, voi -
mat - ter, They are not so proud. No, they
gloi - re, Tes a - mours, Soient de
wa - ter we dis - dain, Drink - ing
Et cou - vert de gloi - re, Chan - te la vic - toi - re
When the drums are roll - ing And the trum - pets blow - ing

À vos beaux dis - cours!
What a jeal - ous crowd.
mours, de tel - les a - mours!
crowd, All your com - mon crowd.
croi - re, l'en croi - re Tou - jours! Vi - dons un
scold me if she finds it out. Come on, com -
là, voi - là mes a - mours!
are, They are not so proud.
boi - - re Tou - jours! Vin ou
keeps us sound and sane! Fill your
Au bruit des tam - bours! Pas de beau - té
We at - tract a crowd. All the pret - ty
ff
ver - re, un ver - re, un
pan - ions, com - pan - ions, One
biè - re, Biè - re ou vin, Que mon ver - re Soit
glass - es, fill your stein, Be it beer, be it
fiè - re, Nous sa - vons leur plai - re, Nous sa - vons leur
lass - es Love a hand - some sol - dier, Oth - ers will be

De vo - tre co -
You don't need to
Vous vou - lez leur
You don't need to
ver - - re de vin! Al - lons, voi -
more ___ glass of wine! Come on, come
Vo - yez leur co -
Oth ers will be
plein, Que mon ver - re Soit plein! Que mon
wine, Be it beer, be it wine. Fill your
plaire En un tour de main, Nous sa - vons leur
jeal - ous, We do not mind. All the pret - ty
lè - re, De vo - tre co - lè - re, De vo - tre co -
tell __ us, You don't need to tell __ us, You don't need to
plai - re, Vous vou - lez leur plai - re, Vous vou - lez leur
tell __ us, You don't need to tell __ us, You don't need to
sin! Al - lons, voi - sin! Vi - dons, vi -
on, A glass of wine! Come on, We'll
lè - re, Vo - yez leur co - lè - re, Vo - yez leur co -
jeal - ous, Oth - ers will be jeal - ous, Oth - ers will be
ver - re, Que mon ver - re, Que mon
glass - es, fill your glass - es, Be it
plai - re, Nous sa - vons leur plai - re, Nous sa - vons leur
lass - es Love a hand - some sol - dier, Oth - ers will be

lè - re Nous ne crai - gnons rien!
tell us, We are not so blind!
plai - re, Nous le sa - vons bien!
tell us, For we know your kind.
dons un ver - re de vin! Vi - dons un
leave our trou - bles be - hind. Come on, com -
lè - re, Vo - yez leur main - tien!
jeal - ous, But we do not mind.
ver - re Soit tou - jours plein! Vin ou
beer or be it wine! Fill your
plaire En un tour de main! Pas de beau - té
jeal - ous, We do not mind. All the pret - ty
cresc.
ff
ver - re, un ver - re, un
pan - ions, com - pan - ions, One
biè - re, Bière ou vin, Que mon ver - re Soit
glass - es, fill your stein, Be it beer, be it
fiè - re, Nous sa - vons leur plai - re, Nous sa - vons leur
lass - es Love a hand - some sol - dier, Oth - ers will be

De vo - tre co -
You don't need to
Vous vou - lez leur
You don't need to
ver - re de vin! Al - lons, voi -
more glass of wine! And now I
Vo - yez leur co -
Oth ers will be
plein, Que mon ver - re Soit plein, Que mon
wine, Be it beer, be it wine, Fill your
plaire En un tour de main, Nous sa - vons leur
jeal - ous, We do not mind. All the pret - ty
8
p
lè - re, De vo - tre co - lè - re, De vo - tre co -
tell us, You don't need to tell us, You don't need to
plai - re, Vous vou - lez leur plai - re, Vous vou - lez leur
tell us You don't need to tell us, You don't need to
sin! al - lons, voi - sin! Vi - dons, vi -
say, And now I say Come on, Let's
lè - re, Vo - yez leur co - lè - re, Vo - yez leur co -
jeal - ous, Oth - ers will be jeal - ous, Oth - ers will be
ver - re, Que mon ver - re, Que mon
glass - es, fill your glass - es, Be it
plai - re, Nous sa - vons leur plai - re, Nous sa - vons leur
lass - es Love a hand - some sol - dier, Oth - ers will be

lè - re Nous ne crai-gnons rien! De vo - tre co -
tell us, We are not so blind. You don't need to
plai - re, Nous le sa - vons bien! Vous vou - lez leur
tell us, For we know your kind. You don't need to
dons un ver - re de vin! Vi - dons un
leave our trou - bles be - hind. Let's leave our
lè - re, Vo - yez leur main - tien! Vo - yez leur co -
jeal - ous, But we do not mind. Oth - ers will be
ver - re Soit tou - jours plein! Vin ou
beer or be it wine! Fill your
plaire En un tour de main! Nous sa - vons leur
jeal - ous, We do not mind. Oth - ers will be
cresc.
f
ff
lè - re Nous ne crai-gnons rien! De vo - tre co -
tell us, We are not so blind. You don't need to
plai - re, Nous le sa - vons bien! Vous vou - lez, vous vou -
tell us, For we know your kind. You don't need to
ver - re, Un ver - re de vin! Vi - dons, vi -
trou - bles and cares be - hind. Let's leave our
lè - re, Vo - yez leur main - tien! Vo - yez, vo -
jeal - ous, But we do not mind, Oth - ers will be
biè - re, Bière ou vin, Que mon ver - re, que mon
glass - es, fill your stein, Strong or mel - low, we don't
plai - re En un tour de main, Nous sa - vons, nous sa -
jeal - ous, But we do not mind. Oth - ers will be
Wind
Strgs.
f
ff

lè - re, De vo - tre co - lè - - - - -
tell us, You don't need to tell
lez, vous vou - lez leur plai - - - - -
tell us, You need not tell
dons, vi - dons un ver - - - - -
cares, Let's leave our trou - - - - -
yez, vo - yez leur co - lè - - - - -
jeal - ous, Oth-ers will be jeal - - - -
ver - re, Que mon ver - re, Que mon ver - - - - -
mind it, Strong or mel - low, Strong or mel - - - -
vons, Nous sa - vons leur plai - - - - -
jeal - ous, They will be jeal - - - -
re Nous ne crai - gnons
us, We are not so
re, Nous le sa - vons
us, For we know your
re, Un ver - re de
bles, leave our cares be -
re, Vo - yez leur main -
ous, But we do not
re Soit tou - jours
low We do not
re En un tour de
ous, But we do not

rien!
blind.
bien!
kind.
vin!
hind.
tien!
mind.
plein!
mind.
main!
mind!

Nº 4. Scene, Recitative, and Cavatina

Valentine.
W.
V.
donc? Quels re-grets at-tris-tent nos a-dieux?_ Comme vous, pour long-
sad? Are you sor-ry that we must de-part?_ I am sad. I con-
f
p
V.
temps, je vais quit-ter ces lieux! J'y lais-se Mar-gue-ri-te, et,
fess, I go with heav-y heart. I leave my on-ly sis-ter, I
p
Siebel.
V.
S.
pour veil-ler sur el-le, Ma mè-re n'est plus là! Plus d'un a-mi fi-
was her sole pro-tec-tor, Our moth-er be-ing dead. You have no cause to
f
Valentine.
S.
V.
dè-le Sau-ra te rem-pla-cer à ses cô-tés! Mer-ci!
wor-ry, I prom-ise to pro-tect her in your stead. Good lad.
f
f

* The French words of this Cavatina are by O. Pradere.

V.
fi - - e. Dai - - gne de
dear to me! Guard her from
tout danger Tou - jours, tou-jours la
harm and ill, Guide her by Thy al -
pro - té-ger, Cet-te sœur si ché-ri - e,
might - y will, Keep her safe and ev-er near to Thee
Dai - gne de tout dan - ger la pro - té -
Lead her up-on Thy way, Thy god - ly
ger, Daigne la pro - té - ger de tout dan -
way, To Thee I hum-bly pray, To Thee I
3

un poco più animato

ger.
pray! _____

Dé - li - vré d'u - ne tris - te _ pen -
I shall fight for _ hon - or _ and

un poco più animato

sé - e, J'i - rai chercher la gloi - re, la gloire au sein des en-ne-mis, Le pre -
glo - ry When bat - tle _ is rag-ing _ a - gainst _ the might-y foe, The

mier, le plus brave au _ fort de la mê - lé - e, J'i-rai com-bat - - tre
first _ to at - tack, the _ brav-est in the fray, Read-y to die _____ if

pour mon pa - ys, Et si, vers lui, Dieu me rap-pel - le,
Fate wills _ it so. And if the Lord choos-es to call ____ me,

Je veil - le - rai sur toi _ fi - dè - le, _____
Then I shall pray _ for you _ in heav - - en,

Tempo I.

Ô_____ Mar-gue-ri - te! A - vant de quit - ter ces lieux,
O_____ Mar-ga - ri - ta! Now that I must say good-by

Sol na - tal de mes a - ïeux, À toi, Sei - gneur et Roi des cieux,
To my home and na - tive sky, Lord, may__ I en - trust to Thee

Ma__ sœur je__con - fi - e! Ô Roi des cieux, jet-te__ les
My__ sis - ter,__ so dear to me, O Lord a - bove, to Thee__ I__

yeux, Pro - tè-ge Mar-gue-ri - te, Roi des cieux!__
pray, Watch o - ver Mar-ga - ri - ta, God a - bove!__

Wagner.

Al - lons, a - mis! point de vai - nes a - lar -
And now, my friends, Let's for - get all our sor -

Allegretto.
Fl. &
Clar.

W.
mes! À ce bon vin ne mê-lons pas de lar - -
row, Leave all your cares, do not think of to-mor - -
mes! Bu-vons! trin-quons! Et qu'un jo-yeux re-
row. Come on! Drink on! And sing a mer-ry
frain Nous met-te en train, nous met-te en train!
song, a mer-ry song to speed us a - long.
Chorus.
TENORS.
BASSES.
Bu-vons! Trin-
Come on! Drink
quons! Et qu'un jo-yeux re-frain Nous mette en train, nous met-te en
on! And sing a mer-ry song, a mer-ry song to speed us a-
Horns

Moderato.
train!
long!
train!
long!
Moderato.
Fl.
Bn.
Wagner.
Un rat plus pol - tron que bra - ve
A rat, dirt - y, grey and ug - ly,
Ob. & Bn.
Vcl.
Et plus laid que beau, Lo - geait au fond d'u - ne ca - ve,
Ver - y big and fat, Once sat in a cel - lar snug - ly,
Allegro.
Mephistopheles.
(appears sudden-ly, interrupting Wagner.)
Sous un vieux ton - neau... Un chat... Pardon!
Un - der an old vat. A cat... That's that!
Vlns.
cresc.

Mephistopheles.
Wagner.
Moderato.
W.
Me.
Hein! Par - mi vous, de grâ - ce, Per - met-tez-moi de pren-dre
What? Would you mind, good peo - ple, If I would join your jol - ly
pp
Me.
pla - ce! Que votre a - mi d'a-bord a - chè - ve sa chan-
gath-'ring, And when your friend is fin - ished with his lit - tle
Me.
3
son! Moi, je vous en pro-mets plu-sieurs de ma fa -
song, I, if you wish, will of - fer you one of my
Wagner.
Me.
W.
çon! U - ne seu - le suf - fit, pourvu qu'el-le soit bonne!
own. Go a - head with your song, I know you will not bore us.
p
Mephistopheles.
Me.
Je fe - rai de mon mieux pour n'en-nuy-er per - son - ne!
I shall try my ver - y best, And you join in the cho - rus.

Nº 4a. Song of the Golden Calf

Me.
cen - se Sa puis - san - - - - - - ce D'un bout du
holds ma - jes - tic pow - - - - - er! Wor-ship the
Me.
gloi - re Dé - ri - soi - - - - - - re Le monstre ab -
rules in pomp and glo - - - - - ry! Wor-ship the
Fl.& Cl.
Me.
monde à l'au - tre bout! Pour fê - ter l'in-fâme i -
might-y Gold-en Calf! Kings and rul - ers kneel be -
Me.
ject in - sulte aux cieux! Il con - temple, ô rage é -
might-y Gold-en Calf! For the sake of its pos -
Vlns.
pp
Horns
Me.
do - le, Rois et peu - ples con - fon - dus, Au bruit
fore him, Great and hum - ble, young and old, None re -
Me.
tran - ge! A ses pieds le genre hu - main, Se ru -
ses - sion, Men at - tack with fire and sword. Mas - ter,
Me.
som - bre des é - cus, Dan - sent u - ne ron - de
sist the lure of gold As they slav - ish - ly a -
Me.
ant, le fer en main, Dans le sang et dans la
serv - ant, knave and lord Join the blood - y, wild pro -

fol- -le, Au- -tour de son
dore him On his throne a-
fan- -ge, Où bril- -le l'ar-
ces- -sion Danc- -ing round his
cresc.
f
pié- -des- tal, Au- -tour de son
bove them all, On his throne a-
dent mé- tal, Où bril- -le l'ar-
ped- -es- tal, Danc- -ing round his
pié- -des- tal! Et Sa- tan conduit le
bove them all. Sa- tan leads the mer- ry
dent mé- tal! Et Sa- tan conduit le
ped- -es- tal. Sa- tan leads the mer- ry
Wind
f
p
bal, con- duit le bal, Et Sa- tan conduit le
ball, the mer- ry ball! Sa- tan leads the mer- ry

Me.
bal, con-duit le bal! Et Sa - tan conduit le
ball, the mer - ry ball! Sa - tan leads the mer - ry
Chorus.
Siebel with the Tenors.
Et Sa - tan conduit le
Sa - tan leads the mer - ry
Wagner with the Basses.
Et Sa - tan conduit le
Sa - tan leads the mer - ry
8
ff Tutti
bal, conduit le bal, con - duit le bal! Et Sa - tan conduit le
ball, the mer - ry ball, the mer - ry ball! Sa - tan leads the mer - ry
bal, conduit le bal, con - duit le bal! Et Sa - tan conduit le
ball, the mer - ry ball, the mer - ry ball! Sa - tan leads the mer - ry
bal, conduit le bal, con - duit le bal! Et Sa - tan conduit le
ball, the mer - ry ball, the mer - ry ball! Sa - tan leads the mer - ry
(2d Verse.)
bal, conduit le bal, con - duit le bal!
ball, the mer - ry ball, the mer - ry ball!
Fine.
Le veau
You shall
bal, conduit le bal, con - duit le bal!
ball, the mer - ry ball, the mer - ry ball!
bal, conduit le bal, con - duit le bal!
ball, the mer - ry ball, the mer - ry ball!
Fine.
p
Dal 𝄋 al fine.

Nº 5. Scene and Chorus.

(taking Wagner's hand and reading his palm)

Me. Ah!___ voi- -ci qui m'at- -tri- -ste pour vous!
Ah, ___ I'm sor- -ry to bring you bad news!

W. Vous vo-yez cet-te li-gne? **Wagner.** Eh bien? **Mephistopheles.** Fâ-cheux pré-
Do you no-tice this line here? And why? A great mis-

Me. sa- -ge! Vous vous fe-rez tu- -er en mon-tant à l'as-
for- -tune! I see that you will die While at-tack- -ing the

Me. S. saut! **Siebel.** Vous ê- -tes donc sor- -cier? **Mephistopheles** (taking Siebel's hand) Tout juste au- -tant qu'il
foe. So you can tell our for-tune? Quite well e -nough, in

Me. faut Pour li- -re dans ta main que le sort te con-
deed, To read there in your palm That when- -ev- - -er you

damne À ne plus tou-cher une fleur Sans qu'el-le se
touch an-y flow-er, My gal-lant friend, it will with-er a-

fa-ne. Moi! Plus de bou-quets à Mar-gue-ri-te!... Ma sœur!
way. What? No more bou-quets for Mar-ga-ri-ta! Hold on!

Qui vous a dit son nom? Pre-nez gar-de, mon bra-ve!
You know my sis-ter's name? Not so dar-ing, my he-ro!

Vous vous fe-rez tu-er par quel-qu'un que je sais!
I say you will be killed By a man whom I know.

(snatching the cup from Wagner)

À vo-tre san-té!
Good health to you all!

(He tastes the wine and throws it from the cup.)
Me.
Peuh! que ton vin est mau-
Phew! What a fla-vor-less
cresc.
ff
Andante.
vais! Per-met-tez-moi de vous en of-frir de ma
wine! If you al-low, I will or-der some from my
dim.
Cornets
p
Allegretto.
ca-ve.
cel-lar.
(striking on a barrel, surmounted by a figure of Bacchus, which serves as a sign for the inn)
Wind
Ho-là! sei-gneur Bac-chus,
Ho there! Bac-chus, my friend!
pp
Tromb.
(Wine flows from the barrel.)
à boi-re!
The fin-est!
Vlns.
pp

Me.
Ap-pro-chez-
Gath-er a-
vous! Cha-cun se-ra ser-vi se-lon ses goûts! À la san-
round! Let ev-'ry-one be served To his own taste! I drink to
té que tout à l'heu-re Vous por-tiez, mes a-mis, à Mar-gue-
her whom all of you know As the fair-est of all, To Mar-ga-
Trombones, etc.
Ob. etc.
Valentine.
Me. V.
ri-te! As-sez! Si je ne te fais taire à l'in-stant, que je
ri-ta! E-nough! I swear that I shall kill you Un-less you are

Allegro.
Wagner. (He draws.)
Mephistopheles (mockingly)
V.
W.
Me.
meu- -re! Ho-là!
si- -lent! On guard!
Pour-quoi trem-
Are you a-
Chorus.
TENORS. f
Ho- là!
On guard!
(draw)
BASSES. f
Ho- là!
On guard!
(draw)
Allegro.
ff
Me.
bler, vous qui me me-na-
fraid? You who threat-en me
(Valentine attacks. His sword breaks in the air.)
Valentine.
Me.
V.
cez? (He traces a circle around him with his sword.)
so?
Mon fer, ô sur-pri-se, Dans les airs se
My sword—it is shat-tered, Split in two by
K. dr.
Moderato maestoso.
V.
bri- se!
mag- ic!
(Valentine and the rest advance on Mephistopheles, holding toward him the cross-shaped guards of their swords. Mephistopheles backs away.)
ff

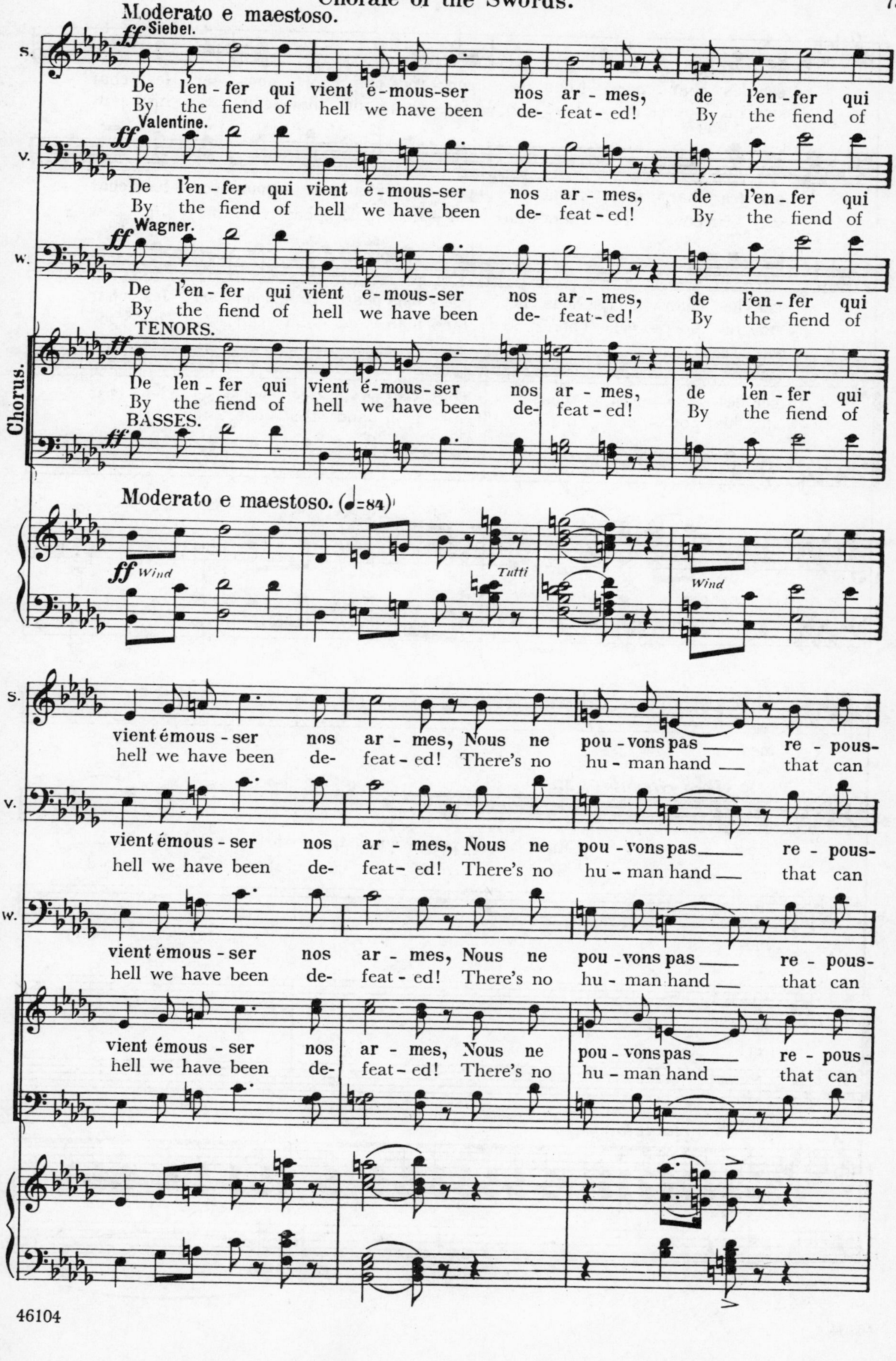

Chorale of the Swords.

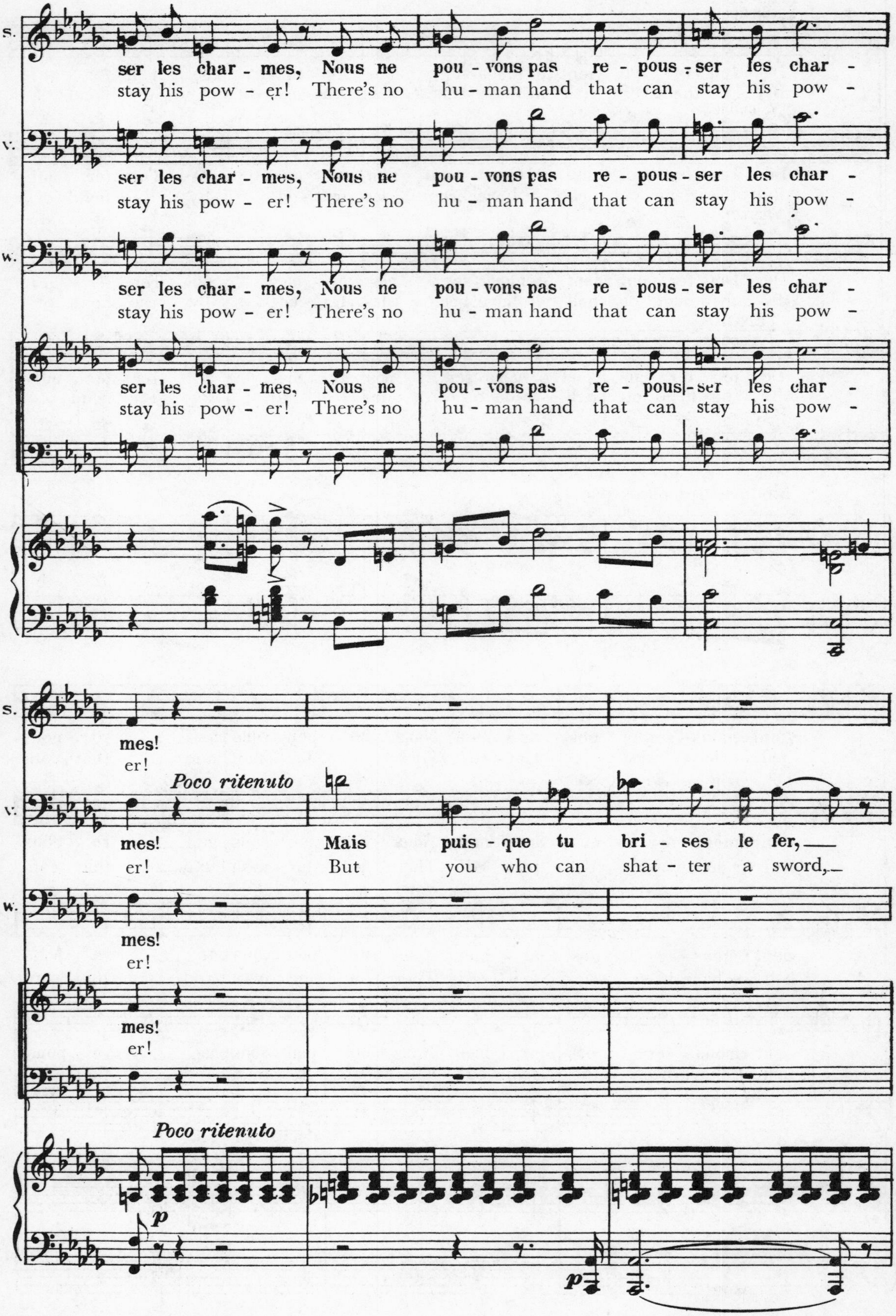

74

S.
Mais puis-que tu bri-ses le fer,
But you who can shat-ter a sword,
V.
Re-gar-
We know
W.
Mais puis-que tu bri-ses le fer,
But you who can shat-ter a sword,
Mais puis-que tu bri-ses le fer,
But you who can shat-ter a sword,
cresc.
re-gar- -de!
We know you!
de! re-gar- -de! C'est
you! We know you! Be-
re-gar- -de!
We know you!
re-gar- -de!
We know you!
Fl., Ob., Cl. Bn., etc.

V.
u - ne croix qui de l'en - fer nous gar - de, C'est
hold this cross which guards us all from e - - vil! Be -
V.
u - ne croix qui de l'en - fer nous gar -
hold this cross which guards us all from e -
Siebel.
S.
C'est u - ne croix qui de l'en - fer nous gar -
Be - hold this cross which guards us all from e -
V.
de! C'est u - ne croix qui de l'en - fer nous gar -
vil! Be - hold this cross which guards us all from e -
Wagner.
W.
C'est u - ne croix qui de l'en - fer nous gar -
Be - hold this cross which guards us all from e -
Chorus.
TENORS.
C'est u - ne croix qui de l'en - fer nous gar -
Be - hold this cross which guards us all from e -
BASSES.
f Tutti

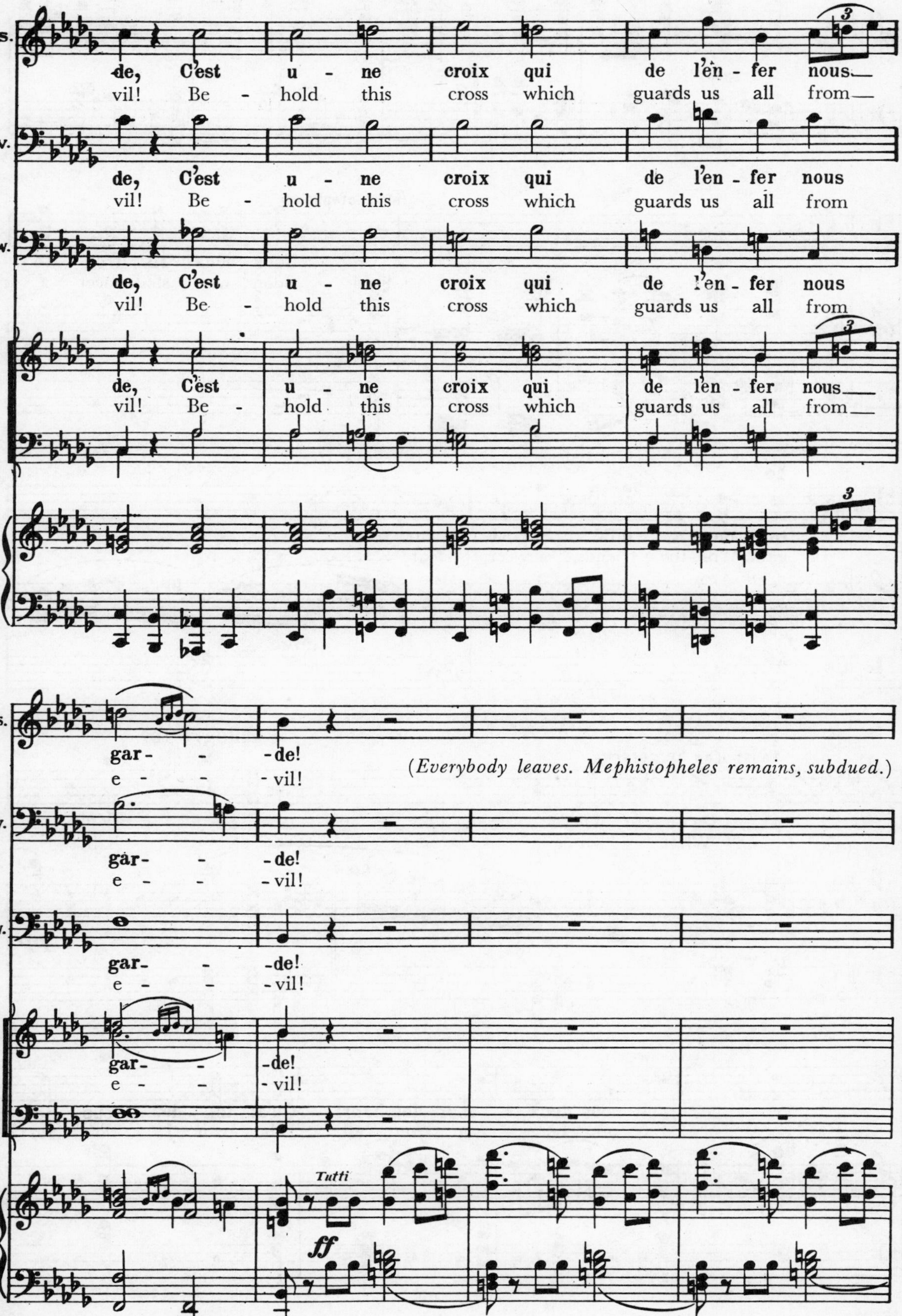

(Everybody leaves. Mephistopheles remains, subdued.)

Mephistopheles.
Me.
Nous nous re - trou - ve -
Soon we shall meet a -
rons, mes a - mis! - Ser - vi - teur!
gain, Wor - thy friends, - nev - er fear!
Ob. & Bn.
f
dim.
Vlns.
p
cresc.
Allegretto.
Faust. (as he enters)
Mephis.
F.
Me.
Qu'as - tu donc?...
What is wrong?
Rien!
Bah!
Fl.
f
Vlns.
pp
À nous deux, cher doc - teur! Qu'at - ten - dez - vous de
I am here at your call, What can I do for

Me.
moi?
you?
Par où com-men-ce-rai- - -je?
My lord, what is your plea- - -sure?
sf
p
F.
Faust.
Où se ca- -che la belle en-
I am long - -ing to see that
Clar.
pp
fant Que ton art m'a fait voir?... est-ce un vain sor-ti-
maid- -en You prom - ised to me. Or was it just an il-
sf
lé-ge?
lu-sion?
Andantino.
Mephistopheles.
Non pas! mais con-tre nous sa ver-tu la pro-té-ge,
Ah no! But she's a pure and a vir-tu-ous maid-en,
Andantino.
Fl., Ob.
p

F.
Qu'im - por-te! je le veux!
No mat-ter, I don't care!
Me.
Et le ciel mê - me la dé - fend!
Heav-en is keep - ing her safe from harm.
f
f
F.
viens! con-duis-moi près d'el - le, Ou je me sé - pa - re de
Come, tell me where to find her, Or I'll stay no long-er with
p
f
F.
toi!
you.
Mephistopheles.
Me.
Il suf - fit! je tiens trop à mon nou - vel em -
Say no more. I have sworn to be your serv - ant on
Ob., Cl.; etc.
pp

Me.
ploi, Pour vous lais-ser dou-ter un ins-tant de mon zè-le. At-ten-
earth, I will not let you doubt my good will for a mo-ment. Stay with
pp
Bn.
Tempo di Valzer. (♩=72)
dons! I-ci même, à ce si-
me. Ver-y soon, as we are
Vns.
p
gnal jo-yeux, La belle et chaste en-
wait-ing here, Your sweet and love-ly
fant va pa-raître à vos
maid, Pure and chaste, will ap-

Nº 6. Waltz and Chorus.

lons La pous-siè - re Des sil - lons, La pous-siè - re
ground, As we dance the mer - ry round To the mu - sic's
lons La pous-siè - re Des sil - lons, La pous-siè - re
ground, As we dance the mer - ry round To the mu - sic's
lons La pous-siè - re Des sil - lons, La pous-siè - re
ground, As we dance the mer - ry round To the mu - sic's
Des sil - lons, Ain - si que la bri - se lé - gè - re Sou-
lilt - ing sound. Light and swift as sum-mer-y breez - es, Our
Des sil - lons, Ain - si que la bri - se lé - gè - re Sou
lilt - ing sound. Light and swift as sum-mer-y breez - es, Our
Des sil - lons, Ain - si que la bri - se lé - gè - re Sou-
lilt - ing sound. Light and swift as sum - mer-y breez - es, Our
lève en é - pais tour-bil - lons La pous-siè - re Des sil - lons,
feet bare-ly touch on the ground, As we dance the mer-ry round
lève en é - pais tour-bil - lons La pous-siè - re Des sil - lons,
feet bare-ly touch on the ground, As we dance the mer-ry round
lève en é - pais tour-bil - lons La pous-siè - re Des sil - lons,
feet bare-ly touch on the ground, As we dance the mer-ry round

La pous - siè - re Des _ sil - lons, Que _ la _ val - se
To the mu - sic's lilt - ing sound. To _ the _ waltz - es'
La pous - siè - re Des sil - lons, Que _ la _ val - se
To the mu - sic's lilt - ing sound. To' _ the _ waltz - es'
p
La pous - siè - re Des sil - lons, Que la val - se
To the mu - sic's lilt - ing sound. To the waltz -
Fl., Ob., Vlns.
pp
nous en - traî - ne! Faites re - ten - tir la plai - ne
sweep-ing _ mea - sure, Hap - py voic - es add - ing plea - sure,
nous en - traî - ne! Fai - tes re - ten - tir la plai - ne
sweep-ing _ mea - sure, Hap - py voic - es add - ing plea - sure,
nous en - traî - ne! Fai - tes re - ten - tir la plai - ne
sweep - ing mea - sure, Hap - py voic - es add - ing plea - sure,
cresc.
De _ l'é - clat de _ vos chan-sons, De l'é - clat de vos chan -
As _ the _ flute and _ trum-pet _ blow, Round and round the danc - ers
De _ l'é - clat de _ vos chan-sons, De l'é - clat de vos chan -
As _ the _ flute and _ trum-pet _ blow, Round and round the danc - ers
De l'é - clat de vos chan-sons, De l'é - clat de vos chan -
As the flute and trum - pet blow, Round and round the danc - ers

sons! Que la val-se nous en-traî-ne!
go! To the waltz-es' sweep-ing mea-sure,
Fai-tes re-ten-tir la plai-ne De l'é-clat de vos chan-sons, de l'é-clat de vos chan-sons!
Hap-py voic-es add-ing plea-sure, As the flute and trum-pet blow, Round and round the danc-ers go.
f
p
pp
dim.
cresc.

Mephistopheles (to Faust)
Me.
Vois ces fil-les Gen-til-les! Ne veux-tu pas
See those charm-ing young maid-ens! Why don't you ask
ff
pp
Aux plus bel-les D'en-tre el-les Of-frir ton bras?
one of them as a part-ner to dance with you?
ff
Faust.
F.
Non! fais trêve À ce ton mo-queur, Et lais-se mon
No! I care on-ly for the one, the love-ly young
pp
cœur À son rê-ve!
girl of my vi-sion.
p

Siebel (enters)
S.
C'est par i - ci que doit pas-
Here I will wait until I
ser Mar - gue - ri - - te!
see Mar - ga - ri - - ta!
Fl. & Vlns.
Non!
No,
SOPRANOS. (approaching Siebel)
Faut - il qu'u - ne fille à dan - ser Vous in - vi - te?
Since when must a girl ask a young man to dance with her?
cresc.
non! Non, non! je ne veux pas val - ser!
no, no, no, I do not want to dance!

SOPRANOS.
TENORS.
BASSES.
Chorus.
Ain - si que la bri - se lé - gè - re Sou - lève en é - pais tour-bil-
Light and swift as sum-mer-y breez-es, Our feet bare-ly touch on the
Vlns.
lons La pous-siè - re Des sil - lons, La pous-siè - re
ground, As we dance the mer-ry round To the mu-sic's
Des sil - lons, Que la val - se nous en - traî - ne!
lilt - ing sound. To the waltz - es' sweep-ing mea - sure,
Fl., Ob., Vlns.

cresc.
Fai - tes re - ten - tir la plai - ne De l'é - clat de
Hap - py voic - es add - ing plea - sure, As the flute and
vos chan-sons, De l'é - clat de vos chan - sons!
trum-pet blow, Round and round the danc - ers go!
f
Faust.
La voi - ci!... C'est el - le!
It is she! I see her!
Mephis.
Eh!
Then
Vlns.
p

Me.
bien! a - bor-dez-la!
speak! Now is the time!
pp
Siebel. (approaches Margarita)
S.
Margue - ri - te! Mau-dit homme!
Mar-ga - ri - ta! Curs-ed med-dler!
Mephistopheles (stepping before Siebel and barring the way)
Me.
Plaît - il?
Not you!
Mephistopheles.
S.
Me.
en-cor là! Eh quoi! mon a - mi, vous voi - là!
You're still here! Of course, my dear boy! So are you!
Me.
ah! ah! vrai - ment! mon a - mi...
Ha, ha! We'll see who will stay!

(Siebel recoils from Mephistopheles who chases him around the scene behind the dancers.)
Me
vous voi - là!
On your way!
(Margarita crosses the stage.)
Andantino (♩ =69)
(One beat equals a measure preceding.)
Faust (accosting Margarita)
F.
Ne permettrez-vous pas, ma bel - le demoi - sel - le,
Will you per-mit me pray, My fair and gra-cious la - dy?
F.
Qu'on vous of - fre le bras pour fai - re le che - min?..
May I give you my arm And es - cort on your way?
Margarita.
Mg.
Non, mon - sieur! je ne suis demoi - sel - le, ni bel - le, demoi -
No, my lord, I am nei - ther a la - dy Nor gra - cious, nei - ther
pp

poco rit.
Ma.
sel-le, ni bel-le, Et je n'ai pas be-soin qu'on me don-ne la
la-dy Nor gra-cious, Nor do I need to be es-cort-ed on my
colla voce
(She leaves.)
a tempo
Faust (gazing after her)
Ma.
F.
main! Par le ciel! que de grâ-ce, et quel-le modes-
way. On my word! She is charm-ing! What mod-es-ty and
F.
ti-e! O belle enfant! je t'ai-me... je t'ai-me... je
can-dor! Beau-ti-ful child, I love you! I love you! I
cresc.
Tempo di Valzer.
Siebel. (coming back)
F.
S.
t'ai - me! Elle est par-ti-e!..
love you! I did not see her!
pp
p
Ped.
Vns.

Mephistopheles. (to Faust)
Eh! bien?
How now?
Faust.
Eh bien!
You ask?
cresc.
On me re - pous - se!
I am re - ject - ed!
f
dim.
p
Mephistopheles (laughing)
Al - lons!
Oh no!
à tes a - mours,
There you are wrong!
Je le vois, cher doc - teur,
In the art of mak-ing love
il faut prê - ter se - cours!
I must help you a - long!
(He goes off with Faust in the direction taken by Margarita.)
Fl., Cl. & Vlns.

cresc.
f
pp
SOPRANOS. (1st Group of young girls.)
Qu'est-ce donc?
What was that?
(2d Group.)
Marguerite, Qui de ce beau seigneur refuse la conduite.
Margarita refused to be escorted By that noble stranger.
Chorus.
TENORS.
f
Valsons! valsons! Valsons!
Dancing! Dancing! Waltzing!
BASSES.
f
Valsons! valsons! Valsons!
Dancing! Dancing! Waltzing!
cresc.

Tutti
Val-sons!.. val-sons!.. Val-sons tou-
Dancing, waltz-ing! On with the
val-sons en-cor!.. Val-sons!.. val-sons!.. Val-sons tou-
On with the dance! Danc-ing, waltz-ing! On with the
val-sons en-cor!.. Val-sons!.. val-sons!.. Val-sons tou-
On with the dance! Danc-ing, waltz-ing! On with the
jours!.. Val-sons tou-jours, Val-sons tou-jours!.. Val-
dance! Let's dance a-gain! Let's dance a-gain! An-
jours!.. Val-sons tou-jours, Val-sons tou-jours!.. Val-
dance! Let's dance a-gain! Let's dance a-gain! An-
jours!.. Val-sons tou-jours, Val-sons tou-jours!.. Val-
dance! Let's dance a-gain! Let's dance a-gain! An-
ff
sons tou-jours!
oth-er dance!
sons tou-jours!
oth-er dance!
sons tou-jours!
oth-er dance!

ff
Ain - si que la bri - se lé - gè - re Sou - lève en é - pais tourbil - lons La pous - siè - re Des sil - lons, La pous - siè - re Des sil - lons, Que la val - se vous en - traî - ne! Fai - tes
Light and swift as sum-mer-y breez - es, Our feet bare-ly touch on the ground, As we dance the mer-ry round To the mu - sic's lilt - ing sound. To the waltz - es' sweep-ing mea - sure, Hap - py
ff
Ain - si que la bri - se lé - gè - re Sou - lève en é - pais tourbil - lons La pous - siè - re Des sil - lons, La pous - siè - re Des sil - lons, Que la val - se vous en - traî - ne! Fai - tes
Light and swift as sum-mer-y breez - es, Our feet bare-ly touch on the ground, As we dance the mer-ry round To the mu - sic's lilt - ing sound. To the waltz - es' sweep-ing mea - sure, Hap - py
ff
Ain - si que la bri - se lé - gè - re Sou - lève en é - pais tourbil - lons La pous - siè - re Des sil - lons, La pous - siè - re Des sil - lons, Que la val - se vous en - traî - ne! Fai - tes
Light and swift as sum-mer-y breez - es, Our feet bare-ly touch on the ground, As we dance the mer-ry round To the mu - sic's lilt - ing sound. To the waltz - es' sweep - ing mea - sure, Hap - py
ff

re - ten - tir la plai - ne De l'é - clat de vos chan -
voic - es add - ing plea - sure, As the flute and trum - pet
sons, De l'é - clat de vos chan - sons!
blow, Round and round the danc - ers go.
Vi -
Più mosso.
ff
f
Jus -
Ex -

qu'à perdre ha - lei - ne, Jus - qu'à mou - rir, Un Dieu les en -
cit - ed - ly swirl - ing, Wild - ly they swing, The danc - ers are
pp
cresc.
traî - ne: C'est le plai - sir!.. Jus - qu'à perdre ha - lei - ne,
whirl - ing, Plea - sure is king! Ex - cit - ed - ly swirl - ing,
Jus - qu'à mou - rir, Un Dieu les en - traî - ne: C'est le plai - sir!
Wild - ly they swing, The danc - ers are whirl - ing, Plea - sure is king!
molto
f
ff

La ter - re tour - noi - - e Et
Their fac - es are burn - - ing, Their
La ter - re tour - noi - - e Et
Their fac - es are burn - - ing, Their
La ter - re tour - noi - - e Et
Their fac - es are burn - - ing, Their
fuit loin d'eux, Quel bruit! quel - le joi -
spir - its high, How fast they are turn -
fuit loin d'eux, Quel bruit! quel - le joi -
spir - its high, How fast they are turn -
fuit loin d'eux, Quel bruit! quel - le joi -
spir - its high, How fast they are turn -
- - - e Dans tous les yeux! La ter - re tour
- - - ing As they fly by! Their fac - es are
- - - e Dans tous les yeux! La ter - re tour
- - - ing As they fly by! Their fac - es are
- - - e Dans tous les yeux! La ter - re tour
- - - ing As they fly by! Their fac - es are
p

noi-e Et fuit, fuit loin d'eux, Quel bruit! quel
burn-ing, Their spir - its are high, How fast, how
noi-e Et fuit, fuit loin d'eux, Quel bruit!
burn-ing, Their spir - its are high, How fast
noi-e Et fuit, fuit loin d'eux, Quel bruit!
burn-ing, Their spir - its are high, How fast
cresc.
-De
bruit! quel-le joi - e Dans tous les yeux!
fast they are turn - ing As they fly by!
quel - le joi - e Dans tous les yeux!
they are turn - ing As they fly by!
quel - le joi - e Dans tous les yeux!
they are turn - ing As they fly by!
ff
Più mosso.
Jus - qu'à perdre ha-lei - ne, Jus - qu'à mou -
See how they are swirl - ing, Wild - ly they
Jus - qu'à perdre ha - lei - ne, Jus - qu'à mou -
See how they are swirl - ing, Wild - ly they
Jus - qu'à perdre ha-lei - ne, Jus - qu'à mou -
See how they are swirl - ing, Wild - ly they
Più mosso.

rir, Un Dieu les en - traî - ne:
swing, The danc - ers are whirl - ing,
rir, Un Dieu les en - traî - ne:
swing, The danc - ers are whirl - ing,
rir, Un Dieu les en - traî - ne:
swing, The danc - ers are whirl - ing,
C'est le plai - sir! Jus - qu'à perdre ha -
Plea - sure is king! See how they are
C'est le plai - sir! Jus - qu'à perdre ha -
Plea - sure is king! See how they are
C'est le plai - sir! Jus - qu'à perdre ha -
Plea - sure is king! See how they are
lei - ne, Jus - qu'à mou - rir, Un
swirl-ing, Wild - ly they swing, The
lei - ne, Jus - qu'à mou - rir, Un
swirl-ing, Wild - ly they swing, The
lei - ne, Jus - qu'à mou - rir, Un
swirl-ing, Wild - ly they swing, The

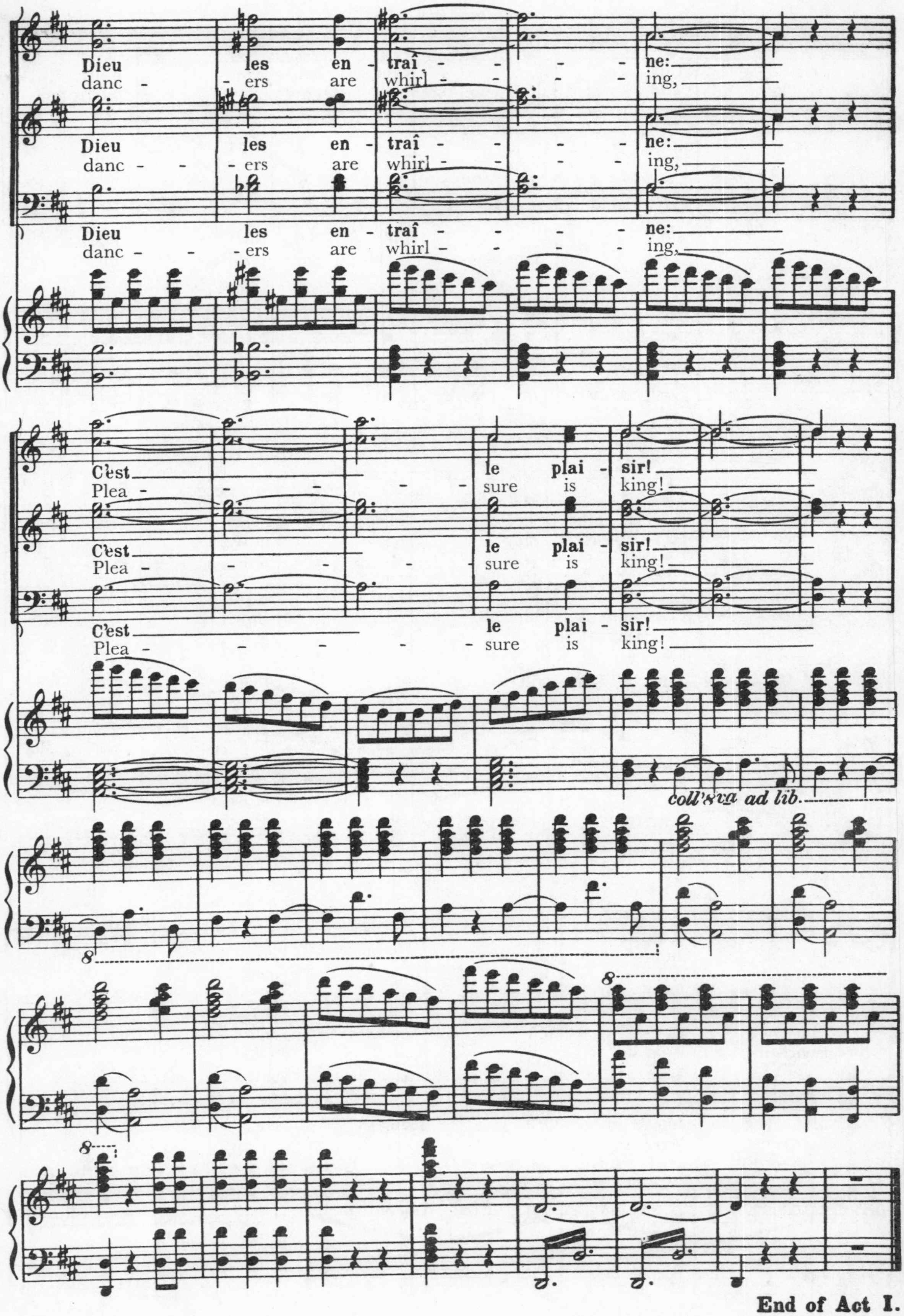

End of Act I.

Act II.

Nº 7. Intermezzo and Song.

Margarita's Garden

A wall at back, with a little door. A bower at left, a house at right, with a window toward the audience. Trees, shrubs, etc.

Moderato quasi andante. (♩ = 60 to 66)

(Curtain rises)
(Siebel enters and stops by a bed of roses and lilies.)
Allegro agitato. (♩.=88)
dim.
cresc.
Cello solo
Siebel.
Fai-tes-lui mes a-
Love-ly flow-ers, be
dim.
veux, Portez mes vœux! Fleurs é-clo-ses près
kind and speak for me! Say I love her sin-

S.
d'el - le, Di-tes-lui qu'elle est bel - le, Que mon cœur nuit et
cere - ly, That I cher-ish her dear - ly, Say my heart is her
cresc.
jour Lan - guit d'a - mour! Fai-tes-lui mes a -
own, And hers a - lone! Will you give her my
veux, Por - tez mes vœux! Ré - vé - lez à son
love And speak for me? Will you bring her a
pp
â - me Le secret de ma flam - me, Qu'il s'exhale a-vec
greet - ing From a heart fond-ly beat - ing? Say my heart ev-er
cresc.
vous Par - fums plus doux!
true Will speak through you!
dim.
p
cresc.

Andante. Recit.
(He plucks a flower.)
S.
Fa-né - - e! hé-las! ce sor-cier, que Dieu
It fad - ed! That man who pos-sessed e-vil
f
colla voce
Tempo I.
(He throws the flower away.)
dam-ne, M'a por-té mal - heur!
pow-er has done this to me!
p
cresc.
Andante. Recit.
Je ne puis, sans qu'elle se fa-ne, Tou-cher u-ne
It is true, when I touch a flow-er It with-ers a-
fp
colla voce
(He dips his fingers in a little font attached to the wall.)
fleur!
way.
Si je trempais mes doigts dans l'eau bé-ni - te!
But if I dipped my hand in ho-ly wa - ter?
Ob. Cl.
Bn.
p
pp
Andante. (♩. = 56)
C'est là que chaque soir vient prier Margue-ri - te! Vo-
It's here that Mar-ga-rite Says her pray'rs ev-'ry eve-ning. And
Fl. Ob. & Cl.
p

Allegro.
(plucking another flower)
yons main-te - nant! voyons vi - te! El-les se fa - nent?..
now let me see! What will hap-pen? Is it fad-ing?
p
p
pp molto cresc.
Tempo I. Allegretto
non!... Sa-tan, je ris de toi! C'est en vous que j'ai
No! You fiend! Your pow-er is gone! Will you give her my
tr
f
dim.
foi; Par - lez pour moi! Qu'el-le puis-se con-naî - tre
love And speak for me? Will you bring her a greet - ing
p
stacc.
L'é-moi qu'elle a fait naî - tre, Et dont mon cœur trou - blé N'a
From a heart fond-ly beat - ing? Say my heart ev - er true Will
cresc.
point par - lé! C'est en vous que j'ai foi! Par - lez pour
speak through you! Love-ly flow-ers, be kind and speak for
pp

S.
moi! Si l'amour l'ef - fa - rou - che, Que la fleur sur sa
me! As her hands fond-ly hold you, Tell her all I have
cresc.
bou - che Sa che au moins dé - po - ser Un doux bai -
told you, That I send with my love A ten - der
dim.
ser! Un bai - ser, un doux bai -
kiss, With my love a ten - der
Fl. etc.
espress.
Ob.
Bn.
p
ser! Un bai - ser, un doux bai - ser!
kiss, With my love a ten - der kiss!
rit.
a tempo
p
colla voce
f a tempo

Scene and Recitative.

(aside, mocking)
Meph.
(returns, unaware of the presence of
Siebel Faust and Mephistopheles.)
S.
Me.
Mon bou - quet n'est - il pas char - mant? Char -
She will love this bou - quet, I'm sure. I'm
Ob.
p dolce
pp
Siebel.
Me.
S.
mant! Vic - toi - re! Vic - toi -
sure! She'll love it! She'll love
S.
re! Vic - toi - re! Je lui ra - con - te -
it! She'll love it! To - mor - row morn - ing
p
S.
rai de - main tou - te l'his - toi - re; Et, si l'on veut sa - voir le se -
I'll re - turn and tell my sto - ry, And then I will re - veal what I

rit.
più lento
S.
cret de_ mon cœur,_ Un bai - ser lui di - ra___ le res -
feel in_ my heart,_ And what words can-not say___ a kiss will im -
più lento
rit.
colla voce
pp
a tempo
Mephistopheles. (mockingly)
(Siebel fastens the bouquet to the door and leaves.)
te! Sé - duc - teur!___
part. Wick-ed man!___
a tempo
sfz
p
Allegro.
(to Faust)
At-tendez-moi là, cher docteur!
You wait for me here, wor-thy friend.
f
Allegretto. (♩=88)
Pour te - nir compa - gnie aux fleurs de votre é - lè - ve, Je
In the mean-time I'll go And find a fit-ting pres-ent To
p
Fl.
Bn.

Me.
vais vous chercher un tré - sor Plus merveil - leux, plus riche en -
vie with the flow-ers of Sie - bel, Some-thing so rare no words can
cresc.
Me.
F.
Faust.
cor Que tous ceux qu'el - le voit en rê - ve! Lais-se-moi!
tell, Far be - yond all im - ag - in - a - tion. Go a - way!
dim.
p
Vcl.
Mephistopheles.
Me.
J'o - bé - is! Daignez m'attendre i -
As you say. But you wait here for
Vln.
Cl.
cresc.
dim.
p
(He leaves.)
Me.
ci.
me.

Nº 8. Cavatina.

Larghetto.

Sa- / How

lut! de-meu-re chaste et pu-re, Sa-lut! de-meu-re chaste et
pure, how chaste this mod-est dwell-ing, How pure, how chaste this mod-est

pu- re, où se de-vi-ne La pré-sen-ce d'une âme in-no-
dwell-ing Where I can feel the gen-tle pres-ence Of her fair and

cen-te et di-vi- ne!... Que de richesse en
in-no-cent be- ing. What bound-less wealth this

cet-te pauvre-té! En ce réduit, que de fé-li-ci-té!
pov-er-ty con-fines, What qui-et bliss from ev-'ry cor-ner shines!

F.
Que de riches-se, que de richesse en cet-te pauvre-té!
What bound-less rich-es, What bound-less rich-es in this house re-side,
Fl.
pp
Ob.
rit.
a tempo
En ce ré-duit, que de fé-li-ci-té!
Where sweet con-tent and hap-pi-ness a-bide!
dim.
pp
colla voce
Poco più mosso. (♩= 56)
Ô na-tu-re, c'est
There, o Na-ture, You
Vln.
p
là que tu la fis si bel-le! C'est
gen-tly formed her ten-der beau-ty, And
là que cette en-fant a dor-mi sous ton
there the love-ly child Rest-ed safe in your

F.
aîle, A grandi sous tes yeux. Là que de ton ha-
arms And ma-tured in your care. There in your ten-der
pp
lei - ne en - ve-loppant son â - me, Tu
keep - ing Her soul was en-shrined in splen - dor; Re-
fis a-vec a-mour é-pa-nou-ir la
spond - ing to your love, The wom-an blos-somed
cresc.
femme En cet an - ge des cieux! C'est là!
forth As an an - gel di - vine! So fair!
dim.
pp
cresc.
Tempo I.
poco rit.
oui! c'est là! Sa-lut! de-meu-re chaste et pu - re! Sa-
Ah! So rare! How pure, how chaste this mod-est dwell - ing, How
Fl. & Clar.
poco rit.
dim. molto
pp
Ped.
Ped.

F.
lut! de-meu-re chaste et pu - re, où se de-vi-ne La pré-
pure, how chaste this mod-est dwell - ing Where I can feel the gen-tle
cresc.
sen-ce d'une âme in-no-cente et di-vi - ne! Sa-lut, sa-
pres-ence Of one who is fair-er than heav - en. So rare! So
dim. pp
lut, demeu-re chaste et pu - - - re,
pure, so chaste this mod-est dwell - - - ing,
cresc.
rit. molto
Adagio.
où se de-vi-ne La pré-sen-ce d'une âme in-no-cen - te et di-
Blessed by the ra-diant light of heav-en And blessed by the beau - ty of her
colla voce
dim.
p
pp
Tempo I.
vi - ne!
be - - ing!
Vlns. etc.
pp
8

Scene.

Allegro assai. (𝅗𝅥 = 92)
Mephistopheles (reentering, carrying a jewel case)
Me.
Piano.
fp
A-ler-te, la voi-là! Si le bou-
Be care-ful! She is here! If his bou-
p
quet l'em-por-te Sur l'é-crin, je con-sens à per-dre mon pou-
quet out-does this case of mine, Then I think it's time that I re-
cresc.
f
p
Faust.
Meph.
Me.
F.
voir. Fu-yons! je veux ne ja-mais la revoir. Quel scru-pu-le vous
sign. A-way! I can't ev-er see her a-gain! Are you out of your
prend?... Sur le seuil de la por-te, Voi-
mind?... Let me put the cas-ket Be-
(puts the casket next to the flowers)
ci l'écrin pla-cé; ve-nez, j'ai bon es-poir.
side Sie-bel's bou-quet; We'll see what she will say.
(Mephistopheles leads Faust away. They hide in the garden.)
Horns
m. d.

Nº 9. Scene and Aria.

Andantino. (♩ = 66)
Piano
pp
Clar.
Bn.
(Margarita enters through the little door and comes silently to the front.)
Vlns.
cresc.
Vln.
pp
dim.
p dolce
p dolce
Margarita.
Ma.
Je voudrais bien sa-voir quel é-tait ce jeune homme;
Who was the hand-some man Who so bold-ly ad-dressed me?
Si c'est un grand sei-
Was he a no-ble
pp
gneur, et comment il se nom - me?
lord? And why has he so im-pressed me?
Ob. & Cl.
dim

Song.
The King of Thule.

Tempo I. (resuming her song)
Ma.
grâ - ce, à ce qu'il m'a semblé. Nul tré - sor n'avait tant de
gra - cious, Or so it seemed to me. And he prized the cup in his
Ma.
char - mes, Nul tré - sor n'avait tant de char - mes! Dans les grands
keep - ing, And he prized the cup in his keep - ing, Drain-ing it
rit.
Ma.
jours il s'en ser - vait, Et chaque fois qu'il y bu - vait,
deep on fes - tive days; And ev - 'ry time it met his gaze
rit.
p
Moderato. (♩= 72)
Ma.
Ses yeux se rem - plissaient de lar - mes!
His eyes would o - ver - flow with weep - ing.
f
Fl & Ob.
p
Quand il sen - tit ve - nir la mort,
Then in his cas - tle by the shore,
f
p

Ma.
É - ten-du sur sa froi-de cou - che, Pour la por-ter jus - -
The old king on his pal-let ly - ing, Know-ing that soon he
rit.
qu'à sa bou-che, Sa main fit un suprême ef - fort!
would be dy-ing, Raised the cup to his lips once more.
Andante.
f
pp
(breaking off)
Je ne sa-vais qu. di-re, Et j'ai rou-gi d'a-bord.
I scarce-ly dared to an-swer, And I was blush-ing so.
(resuming the song)
Et puis, en l'honneur de sa da - me, Et puis,
Tempo I.
And then, with a last brave en-deav - or, And then,
rit.
en l'honneur de sa da - me, Il but u - ne der-niè - re
with a last brave en-deav - or, He drank once more in her mem-o -

più lento
fois.— La cou - pe trem - bla dans ses doigts,—
ry,— Then he threw the cup in the sea —
p.
Et dou - ce - ment il ren - dit l'â - me!
And closed his wea - ry eyes for - ev - er!
Fl
pp
Horns
f
pp a piacere
Les grands seigneurs ont seuls des airs si ré - so - lus, A - vec cet - te dou -
On - ly a lord would have so res - o - lute an air And still ap - pear so
f
Moderato. (She puts the spinning wheel away.)
ceur!
kind.
Al-
O
dolce
cresc.
dim.
p
Ped.
Andante.
lons, n'y pensons plus! Cher Valen - tin! si Dieu m'é -
well, all that is past! — Dear Val-en - tine. may God pro -
cresc.
f

Andantino.
Ma.
cou-te, Je te re-ver - rai! Me voilà tou-te seu - le!
tect you, Bring you safe-ly home. I shall be ver-y lone - ly.
p
dim.
(noticing the flowers)
Recit.
Un bouquet... C'est de Sie-bel, sans dou-te! Pauvre gar-
A bou-quet? It's from Sie-bel, I'm cer-tain. He's a good
f
(She sees the jewel case.)
çon! Que vois-je là? D'où ce
lad. Tempo della Canzone But what is that? Can this
Ob. Bn.
cresc.
ri-che coffret peut-il ve-nir? Je n'ose y toucher,
beau-ti-ful case be meant for me? I hard-ly dare touch it.
pp
et pour-tant... Voi-ci la clef, je crois!.. Si je l'ou-
But per-haps... I see the key to it. What can be

vrais!.. ma main tremble!.. Pour-quoi? Je ne fais, en l'ouvrant, rien de mal, je sup-
in it? I am fright-ened. But why? I won't do an-y harm if I o-pen the
(opens the cover)
po-se! O Dieu! que de bi-joux! est-ce un rê-ve char-
cov-er. Ah no!— It can't be true! Is it real or a
cresc.
f
mant Qui m'é-blou-it,— ou si je veil-le? Mes yeux n'ont ja-mais
vi-sion that I see,— Or am I dream-ing? I've nev-er seen such
f
Allegro non troppo.
vu de ri-ches-se pa-reil-le!
jew-els So pre-cious and gleam-ing!
p
cresc.
(Puts down the casket and kneels to look at the jewels.)

(She takes out the earrings.)

Si j'osais seu-le-ment Me pa-rer un mo-ment De ces pend-ants d'o-reil - le!... Ah! Voi-ci jus-te-ment, au fond de la cas-set - te, Un mi-roir! Com-ment n'ê-tre pas co-quet - te?

If I dared on-ly once To find out how I look In these two love-ly ear - rings? Ah! Here is just the thing! There e-ven is a mir-ror in the case. Who could re-sist such a temp-ta - tion?

Com - ment n'ê - tre pas co -
Who could re - sist such a temp -

The Jewel Song.

Ma.
Ré-ponds-moi, ré-ponds-moi, ré-ponds, ré-ponds, ré-ponds
Is it true? Is it true? Is it real-ly Marga-
cresc.
dim.
vi-te! Non! non! ce n'est plus toi!..
ri-ta? No, no, This is not you!
dolce
p
non... non, Ce n'est plus ton vi-sa - ge; C'est la
No, I see a prin-cess of sto - ry Sweet-ly
cresc.
dim.
p
fil - - le d'un roi, C'est la
smil - - ing back at me, Sweet-ly
Vlns.
fil - - le d'un roi! Ce n'est plus
smil - - ing back at me! This is not
cresc.

Ma.
toi, Ce n'est plus toi, C'est la fil-le d'un roi, Qu'on sa-
you, This is not you! It's a prin-cess or queen Pass-ing
lue au pas-sa-ge! Ah s'il é-tait i-ci!
by in her glo-ry! How hap-py I would be
dim.
p
S'il me vo-yait ainsi! Comme u-ne de-moi-sel-le
If he could look at me! Now if I were to meet him,
a tempo
rit.
pp
Il me trouve-rait bel-le, Ah!
Smil-ing-ly I would greet him, Ah!
Fl.
cresc.
Comme u-ne de-moi-selle Il me trou-ve-rait bel-le,
Then he would bow to me In all my roy-al splen-dor,
f
dim.
p

Ma.
rit.
Comme u-ne de-moi-selle Il me trou-ve-rait bel - le!
Then he would bow to me In all my roy-al splen - dor!
a tempo
Clar.
colla voce
p
Fl.
Vlns.
cresc.
f
Margarita. (She goes back to the jewel case)
A-che-vons la mé-tamor-pho-se.
Now I'll try all the oth-er jew-els!
Clar.
dim.
p
Vlns.
Il me tarde en-cor d'essay-er Le brace-
All I have to do is put on The pret-ty
Poco più lento.
let et le col-lier!
brace-let and the pearls.
trem.

(She puts on the bracelet and the string of pearls.)
Dieu! c'est comme u - ne main,
Ah! It is like a hand
p tornando a poco a poco al tempo I°
qui sur mon bras se po - se! ah! ah!
Heav - i - ly weigh - ing up - on me! Ah! Ah!
cresc.
ah! je ris de me voir Si
Ah! To be sud - den - ly so
f
dim.
pp
belle en ce mi - roir! Ah! je ris de me voir Si
beau - ti - ful to see! Ah! To be sud - den - ly so
leggiero

Ma.
belle en ce mi-roir! Est-ce toi, Margue-
beau-ti-ful to see! Is it you, Marga-
cresc.
ri-te, Est-ce toi? Réponds-moi, réponds-moi,
ri-ta? Is it true? Is it true? Is it true?
p
cresc.
réponds, réponds, réponds vi-te! Ah! s'il é-tait i-ci!
Is it real-ly Mar-ga-ri-ta? How hap-py I would be
dim.
p
S'il me vo-yait ainsi, Comme u-ne de-moi-sel-le
If he could look at me! Now if I were to meet him
a tempo
rit.
pp

Ma.
Il me trouve-rait bel-le, Ah!
Smil-ing-ly I would greet him, Ah!
cresc.
Comme u-ne de-moi-selle Il me trou-ve-rait bel-le! Comme u-ne de-moi-
Then he would bow to me In all my roy-al splen-dor, Then he would bow to
f
dim.
p
rit.
a tempo
selle, Il me trou-ve-rait bel-le! Mar-gue-ri-te,
me In all my roy-al splen-dor! Mar-ga-ri-ta,
pp
colla voce
p
cresc.
Ce n'est plus toi, Ce n'est plus ton vi-sa-ge!
This is not you! That's a prin-cess of sto-ry!

Mz.
Non! c'est la fil - le d'un roi, Qu'on sa -
Yes! It's a prin - cess or queen Pass - ing
f
f
p
Mz.
tr
lue au pas - sa - - - - -
by in her glo - - - - -
Mz.
ge!
ry!
ff

No 10. Scene and Quartet.

M.
là le ca-deau d'un Sei-gneur a-mou-reux! Mon cher é-
deed, some ad-mir-er must have put them there. My hus-band
tr
Bn.
poux ja-dis é-tait moins gé-né-reux!
nev-er gave me a pre-sent so rare!
(Mephistopheles and Faust enter.)
Mephistopheles (saluting)
Me.
Da-me Mar-the Schwerlein, s'il vous plaît?
Mad-am Mar-tha Schwert-lein, I be-lieve?
Martha.
Qui m'ap-pel-le?
Who are you, sir?
f
Tromb.
Vlns.
p
pp
Mephistopheles.
Par-don d'o-ser ain-si nous pré-sen-ter chez vous!
For-give us for in-trud-ing in this way on you!
Cl. & Bn.
(aside to Faust)
(Vous vo-yez qu'elle a fait bon accueil aux bi-
Now you see what a box full of jew-els can

Andante.
Me.
M.
(aloud)
Martha.
Mephis.
joux!) Da-me Mar-the Schwer-lein? Me voi-ci! La nou-
do. Mad-am Mar-tha Schwert-lein? This is she. I am
tr
cresc.
p Bn.
p
Cl. & Bn.
vel-le Que j'ap-por-te n'est pas pour vous mettre en gaî-
sor-ry, I must warn you, You must be pre-pared for the
p
té. Vo-tre ma-ri, ma-da-me, est mort, et vous sa-lu-
worst. Your wor-thy hus-band, Mad-am, Is dead and sends a greet-
f
tr
Martha.
(She faints.)
Margarita.
M.
Ma.
Ah! grand Dieu! Qu'est-ce donc?
What a blow! Are you ill?
(reviving Martha)
e.
ing.
Rien!
No.
ff
pp
f
ff

Martha.
M.
Ô ca-la-mi-té!
Oh, how ver-y sad!
f
p
pp
M.
Ma.
Ô nouvelle im-pré-vu-e!
Oh, how great a dis-as-ter!
Margarita. (aside)
Mal-gré moi mon cœur
In my heart I am
F.
Faust. (aside)
La fiè-vre de mes
My an-guish fades a-
Mephistopheles.
Me.
(to Martha)
Vo-tre ma-
Your wor-thy
Ma.
trem-ble et tres-saille à sa vu-e!
trem-bling At the joy of this meet-ing!
F.
sens se dis-si-pe à sa vu-e!
way At the joy of this meet-ing!
M.
ri, ma-da-me, est mort, et vous sa-lu-e!
hus-band, Mad-am, Is dead and sends a greet-ing.
f

Allegretto.
Martha. (to Mephistopheles)
Ne m'ap-por-tez-vous rien de lui?
What gift has he left me be - hind?
p
cresc.
Mephistopheles.
Rien! et, pour le pu - nir, il
None. And if I were you, I
p.
faut dès aujour - d'hui, dès aujour - d'hui Cher-cher quelqu'un qui le rem-
would pay him in kind And look a - round for some-one bet - ter to re-
pla - ce!
place him.
Faust (to Margarita)
Pour-quoi donc quit-ter ces bi - joux?
Why take off your jew-els so soon?
Margarita.
Ces bi -
Since they
pp

Ma.
joux ne sont pas à moi, lais-sez, lais-sez de grâ-ce...
do not be-long to me, It's wrong, it's wrong to wear them.
Mephistopheles (with affected ardor, to Martha)
Me.
Qui ne se-rait heu-reux d'é-chan-ger a-vec vous La
An-y man would be proud To be cho-sen by you To
f
f
M.
Martha. (aside)
(aloud)
Ah! bah! Plaît-il?
Oh my! You said?
Me.
ba-gue d'hy-mé-né-e! Hé-
be the man you mar-ry! A-
Clar.
sf
dim.
p
Mephistopheles.
Moderato assai. (♩ = 54)
Me.
las! cru-el-le des-ti-né-e!
las! I nev-er had such for-tune!
Vlns.
p
cresc.
Fl.
dim.

Faust. (to Margarita)
Pre-nez mon bras un mo-ment!
Come, let us walk arm in arm!
Margarita.
Lais-sez, je vous en con-ju-re!
I can't. I beg you for-give me!
Mephis. (offering his arm to Martha)
Votre bras...
Your arm!
Martha. (aside)
Il est char-mant!
A charm-ing man!
Mephistopheles. (aside)
La voi-sine est un peu mû-re, La voisine est un peu
This good la-dy is en-dear-ing, But a bit too per-se-
Margarita.
Je vous en con-ju-re! Je vous en con-
Ah, I am too dar-ing! Ah, I am too
Martha.
Quelle noble al-lu-re! Quel-le noble al-lu-re!
What a no-ble bear-ing! What a no-ble bear-ing!
Faust.
Â-me douce et pu-re! Â-me douce et
You are so en-dear-ing! You are so en-
mû-re! Elle est un peu mû-re, Elle est un peu mû-re, un peu
ver-ing! She is quite en-dear-ing, But too per-se-ver-ing, per-se-
Clar.
Bn.
Vlns.
Fl.
Cl. & Bn.
Horn
cresc.

(Margarita takes Faust's arm and they walk together into the garden.)

Ma.
ju - - re!
dar- - ing!
M.
Quel-le noble al-lu - re!
What a no-ble bear-ing!
F.
pu- - re!
dear- - ing!
Me.
mû- - re!
ver- - ing.
dim.
pp
p
cresc.
dim
Vlns.
f
Allegretto. (♩ = 60)
legg.
p
fp
dim.
fp
Martha.
Mephistopheles.
M.
Me.
Ain-si, vous vo-ya-gez tou-jours? Tou-jours!
You mean you trav-el all the time? I do.
Me.
Du - re né-ces-si-té, ma-da - me, Du - re né-ces-si-
Noth - ing that I can do a-bout it, Noth - ing that I can

Me.
té! Sans a - mis, sans pa - rents, sans
do. With-out friends, all a - lone, Un -
Me.
M.
fem - me! Ah!
mar - ried, ah!
Martha.
Ce - la sied en -
When you're young that's
Fl. & Vlns.
pp
M.
core aux beaux jours, Ce - la sied en - core aux beaux jours!
all ver - y fine, When you're young that's all ver - y fine,
M.
Mais plus tard, plus tard! com-bien il est tris - te
But you'll see, you'll see how sad it is lat - er
M.
De vieillir seul, en é - go - ïs - te,
When you are old, a lone-ly bach - 'lor,

M.
seul__ en é-go-ïs-te!
No__ one to con-sole you!
cresc.
dim.
f
Mephistopheles.
Me.
J'ai fré-mi sou-vent, j'en con-viens, J'ai fré-mi sou-
Man-y times, I have to ad-mit, Man-y times, I
tr
fp
fp
vent, j'en con-viens, De-vant cette hor-ri-ble__ pen-
have to ad-mit, At that dread-ful pros-pect__ I__
Fl.
p
Martha.
Me.
M.
sé-e! A-vant que l'heure en soit pas-
shud-der. Then it is best to wait no
dim.
Vlns.
pp
M.
sé-e, Di-gne sei-gneur, son-gez-y bien, A-vant que
long-er, Think of it now while there is time. You would be

M.
l'heure en soit pas-sé-e, Son-gez-y bien, Di-gne sei-
wise to wait no long-er, Think of it now, Think of it
cresc.
dim.
M.
gneur, son-gez-y bien! Son - gez-y
now while there is time, while there is
Mephistopheles.
Me.
J'y son-ge-rai!
That I will do!
pp
M.
poco rall.
Moderato.
bien! son-gez-y bien!
time, while there is time.
(They walk together into the garden. Faust and Margarita re-enter.)
Me.
poco rall.
J'y son-ge-rai, j'y son-ge-rai!
That I will do! That I will do!
Moderato. (♩ = 54)
poco rall.
Clar.
Faust
Margarita.
F.
Ma.
Eh! quoi! tou-jours seu-le? Mon frère est sol-
You say you are lone-ly? My broth-er is a-
Clar.
p
pp
stacc.
Ma
dat; j'ai per-du ma me-re;
sol-dier, I have lost my moth-er.
Fag.

Ms.
Puis ce fut un au-tre mal-heur, Je per-dis ma pe-ti-te
My one lit-tle sis-ter is dead, Since I lost her my heart is
soeur! Pauvre an-ge! pauvre an-ge! el-le m'é-tait bien
sad. Poor an-gel! Poor an-gel! I loved her ver-y
chè-re! C'é-tait mon u-ni-que sou-ci, C'é-
dear-ly! And she was de-vot-ed to me, Yes,
tait mon u-ni-que sou-ci! Que de soins, hé-las! que de
she was de-vot-ed to me. All a moth-er's care I
pei-nes! C'est quand nos â-mes en sont plei-nes Que la
gave her. I tried so ver-y hard to save her, All the

mort nous les prend ain - si, C'est quand nos â - mes en sont
same it was not to be. With all my heart I tried to
Un poco più mosso.
plei - nes Que la mort nous les prend ain - si!
save her, All the same it was not to be.
dim.
pp
colla voce
Fl.
cresc.
Si-tôt qu'el-le s'é-veil-lait, vite il fal-lait que je fusse
From the mo ment she a-woke She want-ed me, no one but
f
pp
Tempo I.
là! El-le n'ai-mait que Mar-gue - ri - te! Pour la
me! Her on-ly love was Mar-ga - ri - ta. If she
cresc.
dim.
pp
voir, la pau-vre pe - ti - te, Je re - pren-drais bien tout ce -
were on-ly here be - side me I would be so hap - py a -

Faust.
Ma.
F.
la! Si le ciel, a-vec un sou-ri-re, L'a-vait fai-te semblable à
gain. If the Lord, smil-ing down from Heav-en, Had cre-at-ed her just like
F.
toi, C'é-tait un an-ge, un an-ge! Oui je_ le
you, She was an an-gel, an an-gel! Dear, just_like
cresc.
dim.
pp
(Mephistopheles and Martha return.)
Margarita. (to Faust)
Ma.
Vous mo-quez-vous?
Are you sin-cere?
Martha. (to Mephistopheles)
M.
Vous n'en-ten-dez pas, Vous n'en-ten-dez pas,
You don't e-ven hear. You don't e-ven hear.
Faust.
F.
crois! Non,
you! No,
Mephistopheles. (to Martha)
Me.
Ne m'ac-cusez pas,
You are wrong, my dear,
poco a poco

M.
Et de moi tout bas Vous ri - ez sans dou - - -
Fur-tive - ly you laugh, You do not be - lieve
F.
non, je t'ad - mi - - -
no, do be - lieve
Me.
Ne m'ac-cusez pas Si je dois me remettre en rou - - -
Ver-y wrong, my dear, But now it's time for me to leave
cresc.
Margarita.
Ma.
Je ne vous crois pas!
In my heart I fear
M.
te! Vous n'en-ten-dez pas,
me! You don't e - ven hear,
F.
re. Lais - se-moi ton bras,
me! Take my arm, my dear,
Me.
te. Ne m'ac-cu - sez pas,
you! No, I am sin - cere.
dim.
p

Ma.
Je ne vous crois pas! Et de moi, tout
You are not sin - cere! Fur - tive - ly you
M.
Vous n'en - ten - dez pas! Ou de moi,
You don't e - ven hear what I say
F.
Lais - se - moi ton bras, Dieu,
Take my arm, my dear, God,
Me.
Ne m'ac - cu - sez pas, Si je dois, hé -
You are wrong, my dear, Grudg - ing - ly, a -
Ma.
bas, Vous ri - ez, vous ri - ez sans doute! J'ai tort de res-
laugh, And I know I should not be - lieve you. I beg you to
M.
tout bas, Vous ri - ez sans doute! A - vant d'écou-
to you, If I could be - lieve you! I beg you to
F.
Dieu ne m'a-t-il pas Con - duit sur ta route? Pour - quoi redou-
God him - self has led me. Could I de - ceive you? My heart speaks to
Me.
las! Si je dois me re - met - tre en route!
las, I as - sure you That I must leave you.
Horn

Ma.
ter Pour vous é-cou - ter...
stay. No, I must not stay...
M.
ter, Pour-quoi vous hâ - ter
stay, Do not go a - way.
F.
pp
ter, Hé - las! re-dou-ter D'é-cou - ter? Mon cœur
you, my love. I im-plore you to stay! I a -
Me.
Faut - il at-tes - ter, at - tes-ter Qu'on voudrait res - ter
And all I can say Is that I would pre-fer to stay,
Vcl.
dim. molto
pp
cresc.
Et pourtant... j'é-cou - te... Et pour-tant... j'é -
Yet I stay... I won - der... Yet I stay... I
pp
De vous mettre en rou - te, De vous mettre en
Must you go, I won - der? Must you go, I
par - le... É-cou - te... mon cœur par - le... é -
dore you, I love you! I a - dore you, a -
pp
Quand on vous é - cou - te, Quand on vous é -
But I have to wan - der, But I have to
pp

Ma.
M.
F.
Me.
cou - te, j'ai tort!
won - der. It's wrong,
rou - te? A - vant d'é - cou - ter
won - der? Must you go a - way,
cou - te! Pour - quoi re - dou - ter D'é - cou -
dore you! And why can't you stay, can't you
cou - te? Faut - il at - tes - ter,
wan - der. All I have to say
cresc.
f
Qui, j'ai tort, et pour - tant j'é -
Yes, it's wrong, Yet I stay and
Pour-quoi vous hâ-ter De vous mettre en rou - te, en
Must you go a-way, Must you real - ly leave me, I
ter? Mon cœur par - le... é -
stay? I a - dore you, a -
Qu'on voudrait res - ter, Quand
I would rath-er stay, But
pp
colle voci

a tempo
Ma.
cou - . - te!..
won - - der!
M.
rou - - te?..
won - - der?
F.
cou - - te!..
dore you!
Me.
on vous é-cou - te?..
I have to wan - der.
a tempo
Vlns.
Fl.
Ma.
Margarita.
Re - ti - rez -
Now you must
Più mosso.
Faust.
Margarita.
Ma.
F.
vous... Voi - ci la nuit! Chère â - me! Laissez -
go... It's get - ting late. My dear - est! You must
Vcl.
pp
(She slips away from him and goes out.)
Faust. (follows her)
Ma.
F.
moi! Ah! méchan - te, on me fuit!
go! Heart-less maid-en! Won't you stay?
Vlns.
Vcl.

Mephistopheles.
(He hides behind a tree.)
Me.
L'en-tre-tien de-vient trop ten - dre, es-qui-vons - nous!
She is get-ting much too friend - ly. Let's slip a - way.
Vln.
Vcl.
Martha (aside)
(aloud)
M.
(Comment m'y pren - dre?)
What shall I tell him?
Eh bien!
You said...
il est par-ti...
Where did he go?
Sei - gneur!
Good sir!
Oui...
Yes!
(runs after him)
Cher sei - gneur!
Wor - thy sir!
cours a - près moi...
Run af - ter me!
Ouf!!!
Ouf!

Me.
cet - te vieille im - pi - to - ya - ble, De force ou de
That old shrew won't be con - tent - ed Un - til some-one
Cl.
gré, je crois, Al - lait é - pou - ser le dia -
mar - ries her, E - ven if it were the dev -
Martha. (off-stage)
M.
Cher sei - gneur!
Dear-est sir!
Faust. (off-stage)
F.
Mar - gue - ri - te!
Mar - ga - ri - ta!
Me.
ble! Ser - vi -
il. Go your
M.
Cher sei - gneur!
Dear-est sir!
F.
Mar - gue - ri - te!..
Mar - ga - ri - ta!
Me.
teur! Ser - vi - teur!
way! Go your way!
pp

Scene.

Andante. (♩ = 54)
Mephistopheles (alone)
Me.
Il é-tait temps! Sous le feuil-la - ge
And none too soon! Un - der the fall - ing
Piano.
p
som - bre Voi - ci nos a-mou-reux qui re - vien-nent!.. C'est
shad - ows The lov - ers are re - turn - ing to - geth - er. All's
Andante.
3
pp
bien!
well.
Gar-dons nous de trou - bler
Let us not in - ter - fere
Vlns.
Fl.
un si doux en - tre - tien!
With a love so sin - cere!
cresc.
rit.

Adagio. (♩ = 50)
Me.
Ô
O
Harp.
p
pp
nuit, é - tends sur eux ton
night! Cast o - ver them your
om - bre! A - mour, fer-me leur
shad - ows! O love! Cap-ture their
pp
p
â - me aux remords im - por -
hearts. Let them feel no re -

Me.
tuns! Et vous, fleurs aux sub-tils par-
morse! You flow'rs, gen-tly un-close and
pp
p
fums, É-pa-nou-is-sez-vous sous cet-te main mau-
bloom. Waft your haunt-ing per-fume Through my sa-tan-ic
Ped.
di-te! A-che-vez de troubler le cœur de Margue-
pow-ers, And suc-ceed in se-duc-ing the heart of Marga-
(He disappears in the shadows.)
ri-te!
ri-ta!
Ped.

Nº 11. Duet.

Andante. (♩= 50)
Margarita. (returning with Faust)
Ma.
Il se fait tard, a-dieu!
It's ver-y late! Good night.
Vlns.
Piano.
pp
cresc.
Vla.
Faust.
F.
Quoi! je t'implore en vain! At - tends!
Must I im-plore in vain? O stay!
Lais - se ta main s'ou-bli-er dans la mien-ne.
Let me but hold your dear hand in my own.
Lais - se-moi, lais - se-moi
Bless - ed love, bless - ed love,
pp

F.
con-templer ton vi - sa - ge, Lais - se-moi con-tem -
Let me mar-vel in rap - ture, Let me gaze on your
pler ton vi - sa - - ge! Sous la pâ -
face, Lost in won - - der, As the pale
Horns
le clar - té Dont l'as - tre de la nuit,
moon a - bove Shines through the dark of night
Fl.
com-me dans un nu - a - ge, Ca - res - se, ca - res - se ta beau -
From the star-ry heav-en yon-der Ca - ress - ing, ca - ress-ing you, my
Hns.
Ob.
colla voce
a tempo
Margarita.
F.
Ma.
té! Ô si - len - ce... ô bonheur! i - nef - fa - ble mys -
love. Bless-ed si - lence, joy un-known, How sub-lime is your
a tempo
Vlns.
pp

tè - re! ô bonheur! i - nef - fa - ble mys - tè - -
mys - t'ry! Joy un-known, How sub - lime ___ is your mys - -
re!.. En - i - vran - te lan - gueur!... J'écoute et
t'ry! By your spell I am bound, ___ I hear a
Bn.
je com - prends ___ cet - te voix ___ so - li - tai - re Qui
mag - ic sound, ___ One sweet voice ___ so be - guil - ing, En -
Fl.
Cl.
a tempo
(taking her hand away from him)
chan - te, qui chan - te dans mon cœur!... ___
chant - ing, en - chant - ing All my heart! ___
colla voce
pp a tempo
Faust.
Lais-sez un peu, de grâ - ce... Qu'est-ce
Now I must ask a fa - vor. Won't you

Margarita (plucking the petals from a flower)
F.
Ma.
donc?.. Un sim - ple jeu! Lais -
say? A sim - ple game! Don't
Ma.
F.
Faust.
sez, lais - sez un peu! Que dit ta bouche à voix
look, it won't take long. What is it that you are
Fl.
F.
Ma.
Margarita.
bas - se? Il m'ai - me, Il ne m'ai - me
whis - p'ring? He loves me... he loves me
Ob.
Fl.
Ma.
pas, Il m'ai - me... pas... Il m'ai - me... pas... Il
not... He loves me... not... he loves me... not... He
Vlns.
Ob.
cresc.

Faust.
Ma.
F.
m'ai - me!.. Oui, crois en cet - te fleur é - clo - se sous tes pas... Qu'el-le soit pour ton cœur l'o-ra - cle du ciel mê - me!... Il t'ai - me! comprends-tu ce mot sublime et doux? Ai -
loves me! Yes, be - lieve in this word, The flow - er tells you true! What your own heart has heard Must be the voice of heav - en. He loves you! Do you know what hap-pi-ness it means? To
f animato poco a poco
cresc.
f
dim.

F.
mer! Por - ter en nous une ar -
love, to know the flame That will
Harp.
pp
deur tou - jours nou - vel - le!...
bind two souls to - geth - er,
Nous en - i - vrer sans fin d'u - ne
And brings ec - stat - ic joy To our
cresc.
joie é - ter - nel - le!
hearts nev - er - end - ing.
dim.
mf
Adagio.
Margarita.
p
Ma.
É - ter - nel - le!..
Nev - er end - ing!
Adagio.
É - ter - nel - le!..
Nev - er end - ing!
Clar.
Bn.

pp
É-ter-nel-le!..
Nev-er end-ing!
Andante. (♩= 50)
ppp
É-ter-nel-le!..
Nev-er end-ing!
Ô nuit d'a - mour! ciel ra-di-eux! Ô douces flam-mes! Le bon-heur si-len-ci-eux Ver-se les cieux, les cieux Dans nos deux â - mes!
Oh night of love, oh ra-diant sky! Oh sweet sur-ren - der! Love's de-light, sweet and se-rene, Pour in our hearts your joys In all their splen - dor!
Vlns.
pp
p
Hns.
Vcl.
poco cresc.
dim.
Margarita.
Je veux t'ai-mer et te ché-rir! Parle en - co - re! Je t'ap-par-tiens! je t'a-do - re! Pour toi je veux mou - rir!
You are my love, my life, my own, I a - dore you! My heart is yours, I a - dore you, I'll live for you a - lone!
dim.
Fl., Clar., etc.
ppp
Harp.
Ped.

Ma.
Par - le... parle en - co-re!.. Ah! je t'a-
Dear - est, say you love me! Ah, I a-
Ped. Ped. Ped. Ped.
rit.
do-re! Pour toi je veux mou-rir, pour toi je veux mou-rir!
dore you, I live for you a-lone, I live for you a-lone.
rit.
Allegro agitato.
(She tears herself away from his embrace.)
Ah! par - tez!..
Ah, no more!
Faust.
F.
Mar - gue - ri - te! Mar - gue-
Mar - ga - ri - ta! Mar - ga-
Allegro agitato. (𝅗𝅥=76)
f p p
Ah! par - tez! Je chan-cel - le!
Ah, no more! I am fright ened!
ri - te! cru-el - le... Me sé - pa-
ri - ta! I beg you! Don't make me
cresc.

Ma.
F.
Lais-sez - moi!
You must go!
Lais-sez -
You must
rer de toi! cru - el - le!
leave you now! I beg you!
f
moi! Lais - sez - moi! Lais - sez - moi! Ah!
go! Leave me now! You must go! Ah!
Me sé - pa-rer de toi!..
Why must I leave you now?
ff
Horns
(𝅗𝅥 = 66)
— par-tez, par-tez, oui, partez vi-te... Partez, je
— You must not stay, leave me. I beg you, You must not
pp
poco rall.
tremble, hé-las!.. j'ai peur! Ne brisez pas le cœur de Margue-
stay! I'm so a - fraid! Please do not break my heart, My dear be-
poco rall.

Tempo I.
Ma.
ri - te! Ne bri-sez pas le cœur de Margue - ri - te! Partez! je
lov - ed. Please do not break my heart, My dear be - lov - ed! De-part! I
pp
cresc.
Ma.
tremble, hélas! j'ai peur! Ne bri - sez pas le cœur de Margue -
beg you, I am a - fraid! You must not break my heart, My dear be -
f
dim.
p
pp
un poco rit.
Ma.
F.
Faust.
ri - te! Tu veux, tu veux que je te
lov - ed. My love! You ask that I should
colla voce
un poco rit.
F.
quit - te! Vois ma dou - leur, hé - las! vois ma dou - leur!.. Mar - gue -
leave you? See my de - spair, my love! See my de - spair, Mar - ga -
rit.
F.
ri - te! Mar - gue - ri - te! tu me bri - ses, tu me bri - ses le
ri - ta! Mar - ga - ri - ta! You are break-ing, you are break-ing my
cresc.
rit.
dim.

Margarita.

Si je vous suis chè - re,
If you real - ly love me,

cœur!.. Par pi - tié!__
heart!__ Let me stay!__

Mar - gue -
Mar - ga -

Par__ votre a - mour, par ces a - veux Que je de - vais
Then__ do not stay. By all your vows, By the love you

ri - te!..
ri - ta!

tai - re, Cé - dez à ma pri - è - - re, cé - dez à__ mes
bear me, I beg of you have mer - - cy, Be - lov - ed,__ I

vœux!.. Partez, par - tez, oui, par - tez vi - te! Partez, je
pray. You must not stay, leave me, I beg you, You must not

Faust.
Tu veux, hé - las! que je te quit - te, Vois ma dou -
You ask, a - las, that I should leave you? See my de -

Ma.
trem - ble, hé - las! j'ai peur! Ne bri - sez
stay! I'm so a - fraid! Ah, do not
F.
leur, Vois ma dou - leur!
spair, You break my heart!
Ma.
pas le cœur de Mar - gue - ri - te!.. Ne bri - sez
break my heart, My dear be - lov - ed! Ah, do not
F.
Tu me bri - ses le cœur!
You are break - ing my heart!
Ma.
pas le cœur de Mar - gue - ri - te! Par - tez, je
break my heart, My dear be - lov - ed. De - part, I
F.
Tu me bri - ses le cœur! Mar - gue -
You are break - ing my heart! Mar - ga -
cresc.
Ma.
trem - ble, hé - las! j'ai peur! Ne
beg you, I am a - fraid! Ah,
F.
ri - te! Mar - gue - ri - te!
ri - ta! Mar - ga - ri - ta!
f
dim.

=De
a tempo
bri-sez pas le cœur de Mar-gue - ri - te! Partez, par-
do not break my heart, My dear be - lov - ed! Ah, do not
Tu me bri-ses le cœur! Vois ma dou-
You are break-ing my heart! See my de-
p
pp
colla voce
a tempo
cresc.
tez, Hé-las! je trem - ble! par - tez, par - tez... j'ai
stay, My love, I beg you. My love, You break my
leur! Mar - gue - ri - te! Vois ma dou -
spair, Mar - ga - ri - ta! You break my
f
peur!
heart!
leur!
heart!
ff
Clar.
rit. dim.
Moderato.
p
rit.

Andante *(tempo dell'aria di Faust)*.

Faust. *(mastering his emotion)*

Di - vi - ne pu - re - té!.. Chaste in - no -
Di - vine ___ and blame-less maid, ___ Chaste as a

espress.

cen - ce, Dont la puis - san - ce Tri - om - phe de ma vo - lon -
flow - er, Yours is the pow - er That tri - umphs o - ver my de -

Più mosso. **Margarita.**

té!.. J'o - bé - is!.. mais de - main... Oui, de - main, dès l'au -
sire. I o - bey. But to - mor-row, Yes, to - mor-row— that I

Più mosso. **p**

ro - re, de - main, ___ tou - jours!..
prom - ise, At dawn ___ of day! **Faust.**

Un mot en - co -
Be - fore I leave

cresc. *dim.* *cresc.*

re! ré - pè - te - moi ce doux a - veu! Tu m'ai - mes?
you, Tell me those pre - cious words once more! You love me?

dim. **p** *cresc.* *dim.*

(*Margarita, hastening toward the house, stops for an instant on the threshold and throws a kiss to Faust.*)

F.
Vlns.
p
cresc.
Margarita.
Faust.
Ma.
F.
A - dieu!
A - dieu!
Fé - li - ci - té du ciel!
Oh ec - sta - sy di - vine!
f
ff
K.-dr.
Allegro.
Ah! fu - yons!
Ah! A - way!
(He starts for the garden door. Mephistopheles bars his way.)
Tu nous é - cou - tais?
So you play the spy?
Mephistopheles.
Me.
Tê - te fol - le!
You're a mad - man!
Par bonheur!
To be sure!
Moderato.
Vous au - riez grand be -
It real - ly seems to
pp
Vcl.

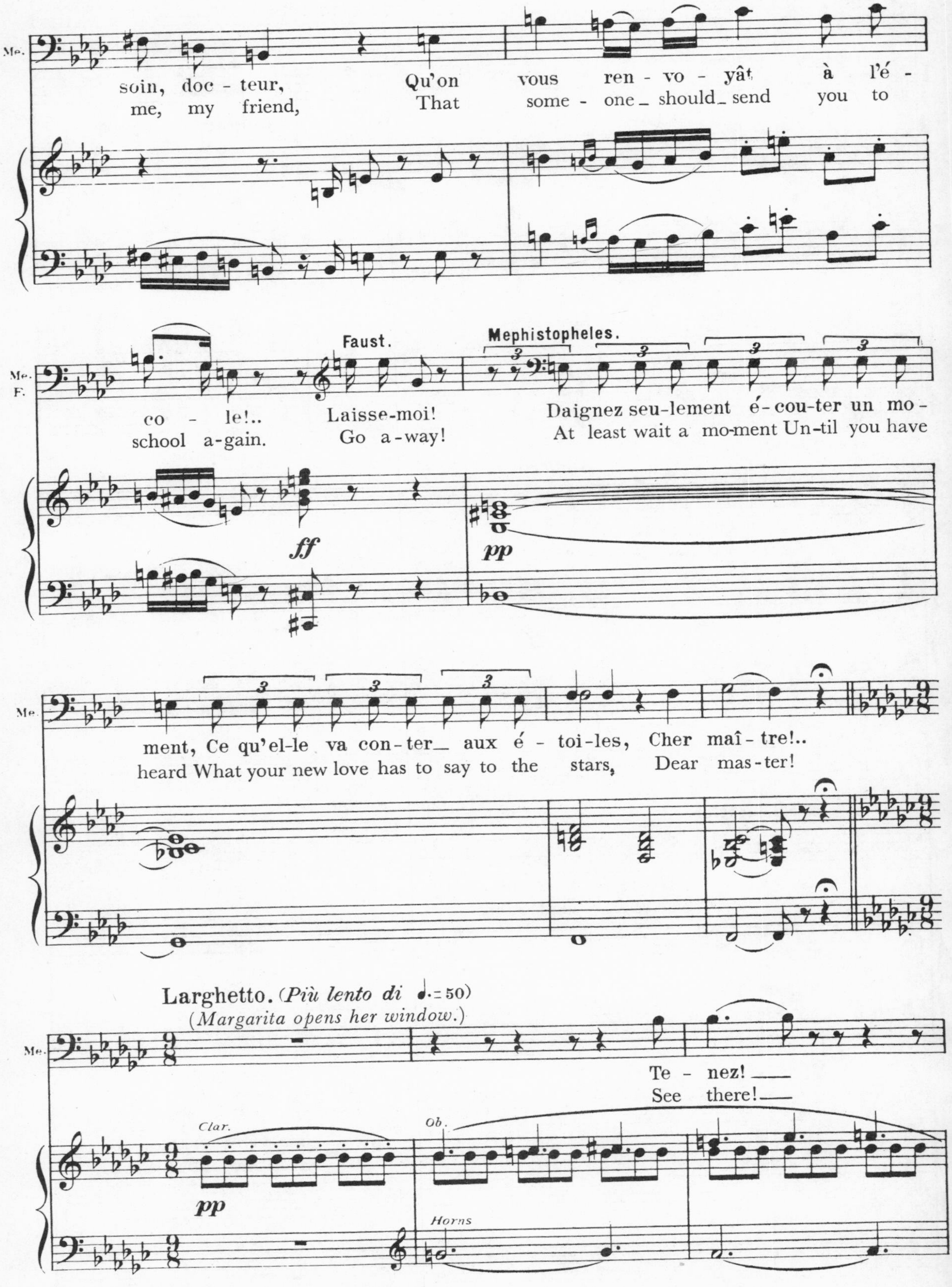

174

Margarita.
Me.
Ma.
Elle ou - vre sa fe - nê - tre... Il
She o - pens her win - dow... He
Fl.
poco cresc.
dim.
pp dolcissimo
Ma.
m'ai - me! il m'ai - me! Quel trouble en mon
loves me! He loves me! My heart o - ver -
8
Ma.
cœur! L'oi-seau chan - te,
flows! The birds are sing - ing,
Oh.
Fl
Ma.
cresc.
Le vent mur - mu - re! Tou-tes les voix de la na -
The breez-es mur - mur! All the voic - es of cre -
Clar.

Ma.
ff
tu - re Me re - di-sent en chœur «Il t'ai - me!
a - tion Are re - peat-ing the words: "He loves you!
cresc
f
dim.
pp
Il t'ai - me!» Ah! qu'il est doux de
He loves you!" Ah, what a joy in
pp
Ped.
vi - vre! Le ciel me sou - rit; L'air m'en-
liv - ing! The night fills my heart with its
dim.
i - vre, l'air m'en - i - vre!
glo - ry and en - chant - ment!
p
pp
Est - ce de plai-sir et d'a - mour Que la feuil-le tremble et pal-
Ev-'ry-where with plea-sure and love All the leaves are trem - bling and

pi - te? De - main, de -
sigh - ing. My love! My
cresc.
main! ah! pres - se ton re -
love! Ah, do not lin - ger
tour, cher bien - ai - mé! Viens!
long So far a - way! Come!
cresc. molto
(She gives herself to Faust's embrace. Mephistopheles laughs loudly and cynically as he leaves the garden.)
viens! ah!
Come! Ah!
Faust.
(rushing to the window) Mar - gue - ri - te!
Mar - ga - ri - ta!
Mephistopheles.
Hein!
Ha, ha, ha, ha, ha!
sempre cresc.
f
cresc.

End of Act II.

Act III.

Entr'acte and Recitative.

SCENE 1

Margarita's Room

p
rit.
Adagio.
Margarita.
Ma.
El-les ne sont plus
They all have gone a-
a tempo
Clar.
pp
Ma
là... je ri-ais a-vec el-les Au-tre-fois... maintenant...
way... Once I shared in their laugh-ter, Long a-go... but no more...
pp
Allegretto vivo.
SOPRANOS (off-stage)
Le ga-lant é-tran-ger s'en-fuit et court en-
The gal-lant strang-er ran a-way! Where did he
pp
Vla.
cor! Ah! ah! ah! ah! ah! ah! ah! ah! ah! ah! ah! ah!
go? Ha ha! ha ha! ha ha ha ha ha ha ha ha!
Vcl.
f

No 12. The Spinning-wheel Song.

Scene.

Moderato.
Recit.
Marg.
Piano.
El - les se ca - chaient! ah! cru - el - les!
They have gone a - way! Ah, they scorn me!
Je ne trouvais pas d'outrage assez fort, Ja - dis, pour les péchés des
Not so long a - go I could not find words too strong for oth - er peo - ple's
autres! Un jour vient où l'on est sans pi - tié pour les nôtres! Je ne
vic - es, and to - day it is they who will show me no pit - y. In my
suis que hon - te à mon tour! Et pour - tant
turn I must suf - fer too! But it's true,
Dieu le sait, je n'é - tais pas in - fâ - me; Tout
heav - en knows, I had no thought of e - vil; My
dim.
pp
p
Cl

(1) In the theatre a cut is made between ⊕ and ⊕ on p. 188.

Ma.
pas!.. J'ai peur, je fris-son - ne; Je lan-guis, hé-
turn, I weep, I am lone - ly. How I long and
las! En vain l'heu - re son - ne; Il ne re-vient
yearn, I wait for him on - ly, He does not re-
a piacere
a tempo
pas! Où donc peut-il é - tre?..
turn. O where does he wan - der?
Seule a ma fe-nê - tre, Je plon - ge là-bas Mon re-
Far in-to the dis - tance I gaze and I mourn As I
gard, hé - las! hé - las! Où donc peut-il
wait for him and yearn! O where does he
dim.

a piacere
a tempo
Ma.
ê - tre?.. Il ne re-vient pas!
wan - der? He does not re - turn!
pp
Ma.
Fl. & Cl.
Je n'o - se me
My grief, I must
Ma.
plain - dre,
bear it,
Il faut me con -
With none can I
p
Ma.
train - dre!
share it!
Je pleu - re tout
No more can I
p

Ma.
bas, Je pleu - re tout
sleep, I wake and I
cresc.
p
bas; S'il pouvait con - naî - tre Ma dou-leur! he -
weep! All my grief and sor - row Are to him un -
cresc.
las! Où donc peut-il ê - tre?.. Il ne re - vient
known! O where does he wan - der? He does not re -
a piacere
dim.
pp
a tempo
pas! Oh! le
turn! O, I

Ma.
voir, en-ten-dre Le bruit de ses pas. Mon cœur est si
wait, I wait for his step at the door. My poor heart is
cresc.
Ma.
las, Si las de l'at-ten-dre! Il ne re-vient
sore, So wea-ry of wait-ing, He does not re-
Ma.
pas, Il ne re-vient pas! Mon sei-gneur, mon sei-
turn, He does not re-turn! Gra-cious Lord, gra-cious
f
Allegro.
Ma.
gneur, mon maî-tre! S'il allait pa-raître, S'il allait pa-
Lord Al-might-y! Could I see him be-fore me, Could I see him be-
ff Wind
f

Ma.
raî - tre, quel - le joi - - e!
fore me, I would be so hap - - py!
ff
Tempo I.
Ma.
Hé - las! hé - las! Où donc peut - il ê - tre?
A - las, a - las! o where does he wan - der?
pp
Ma.
Il ne re - vient pas!
He does not re - turn!
pp
Allegro agitato.
(Siebel enters hurriedly.)
p
cresc.
f
(1)

(1) Dal 𝄋 page 188.

(Siebel enters hurriedly.)

Allegro agitato.

mour!
true. —

cresc. — — — — — f

Margarita.

Sie-bel!   Hé-las! vous seul ne me maudissez
Sie-bel!   A - las, the on-ly faith-ful friend I

Siebel.

Mar-gue-ri - te!   En-cor des pleurs!
Mar-ga - ri - ta!   In tears a - gain!

Moderato.

p

Siebel

3   3   3   3   3

pas... Je ne suis qu'un enfant;   mais j'ai le cœur d'un homme,   Et je vous ven-ge-
have. I am still ver-y young   But a man   in spir-it,   And I swear I'll a-

p f

Margarita.

Qui donc?..
Whom?

rai de son lâche a-ban - don,   Je le tue - rai!   Faut-
venge All the wrong he has done. I'll strike him dead!   You

f ff

Cl.& Bn.

Ma.
Non, tai-sez-
No, say no
S.
il que je le nomme?.. l'in-grat qui vous tra - hit!..
ask — me to name him, The vil-lain who be - trayed you?
f
Clar.
Un poco animato.
Misurato. Andante.
Ma.
vous!..
more!
Oui! tou -
Yes, I
S.
Par-don! vous l'ai-mez en-co - re?
For-give! Then you still love him?
Un poco animato.
Andante.
p
Vcl.
Recit.
Ma.
jours! tou-jours! Mais ce n'est pas à vous de plaindre mon en-nui, J'ai
do! I do! But I have no right to bur-den you like this, I'm
fp
(Siebel takes Margarita's hand)
Ma.
tort, Sie-bel, de vous par-ler de lui.
wrong, my friend, To speak of him to you.

Romance.   Siebel.

Andante.

Si le bon-
When you are

heur _ à sou-ri_re t'in-vi-te, Jo-yeux a-lors je sens un doux é-
glad _ And the sun _ is shin-ing, Then, Mar-ga-ri-ta, I am hap-py

moi; Si la dou-leur _ t'ac-ca-ble, Mar-gue-ri-te, Ô Mar-gue-
too; But when in grief _ and mourn-ing you are pin-ing, O Mar-ga-

ri-te, Ô Mar-gue-ri-te, je pleure a-lors, je pleu-re com-me
ri-ta, O Mar-ga-ri-ta, I weep with you. I weep and grieve with

toi!
you!

S.
Com - me deux fleurs sur u - ne mê - me ti - ge, No - tre des -
As twin-stars wan-der in the sky to - geth - er, So we are
p
tin sui-vant le mê - me cours, De tes cha - grins en frè - re je m'af -
des-tined to one com - mon end. I want to share your suf-fer-ing for -
cresc.
fli - ge, Ô Mar-gue - ri - te, Ô Mar-gue - ri - te, Comme u-ne sœur je t'ai-me-rai tou -
ev - er, O Mar-ga - ri - ta, O Mar-ga - ri - ta. Yes, I shall al-ways love you as a
sfz
dim.
jours, je t'ai - me - rai tou - jours, je
friend, I shall love you as a faith - ful friend, I shall
t'ai - me - rai tou - jours!
love you as a faith - ful friend.

Margarita
Ma.
So-yez bé-ni, Sie-bel; votre a-mi-tié m'est douce!
May heav-en smile on you, For you are good to me.—
p
Ceux dont la main cru-el - le me re-pousse N'ont pas fer-mé pour
All those who now dis-dain me as a sin-ner Can still not bar the
p
p
p
moi— les por-tes du Saint-lieu!.. J'y vais, pour mon en-fant et pour
way— To God who will for-give.— I'll go, for my child and for
lui pri-er Dieu!..—
him I shall pray!—
dim.
pp
cresc.
Ped.
Ped.
dim.
Ped.
Ped.
p
pp

№ 13. Scene in the Church.

SCENE 2

Andante.

(Some women enter the church. Margarita enters after them and kneels.)

Margarita
Ma.
Seig-neur, daignez per-mettre à votre humble ser-van-te De—
O Lord, Thy hum-ble serv-ant is ask-ing Thy mer-cy, See—
Ma.
— s'a-genouil-ler de-vant vous.
— me kneel be-fore Thee and pray.
(Organ)

Mephis. (appears behind a pillar)
Me.
Non! tu ne prie-ras pas! Non! tu ne prie-ras
No! you shall pray no more! No! you shall pray no
pas! Frap-pez-la d'é-pou-van-te! Esprits du mal,
more! All ye spir-its of e-vil, Gath-er a-round,
fp (Orch.)
fp
fp
3
accou-rez tous!
tor-ture her heart!
fp
fp
f
Wind
6
ff
Chorus of Demons (off-stage)
Mar-gue-
Mar-ga-
Vlns.
Wind
dim.
Vlns.
pp

Margarita.
Ma.
Qui m'ap-pel - - le?
Who calls me?
ri - - - te! Mar - gue -
ri - - - ta! Mar - ga -
Ma.
Je chan-cel - le!.. je meurs!.. Dieu
I am fright-ened! I'll die . . . Dear
ri - - - te!
ri - - - ta!
cresc.
Ma.
bon! Dieu clé - ment! est - ce dé -
God, God of mer - cy! Has the day of
Ma.
jà l'heu - re du châ - ti - ment?
Judg - ment al-read-y ar-rived?
dim.

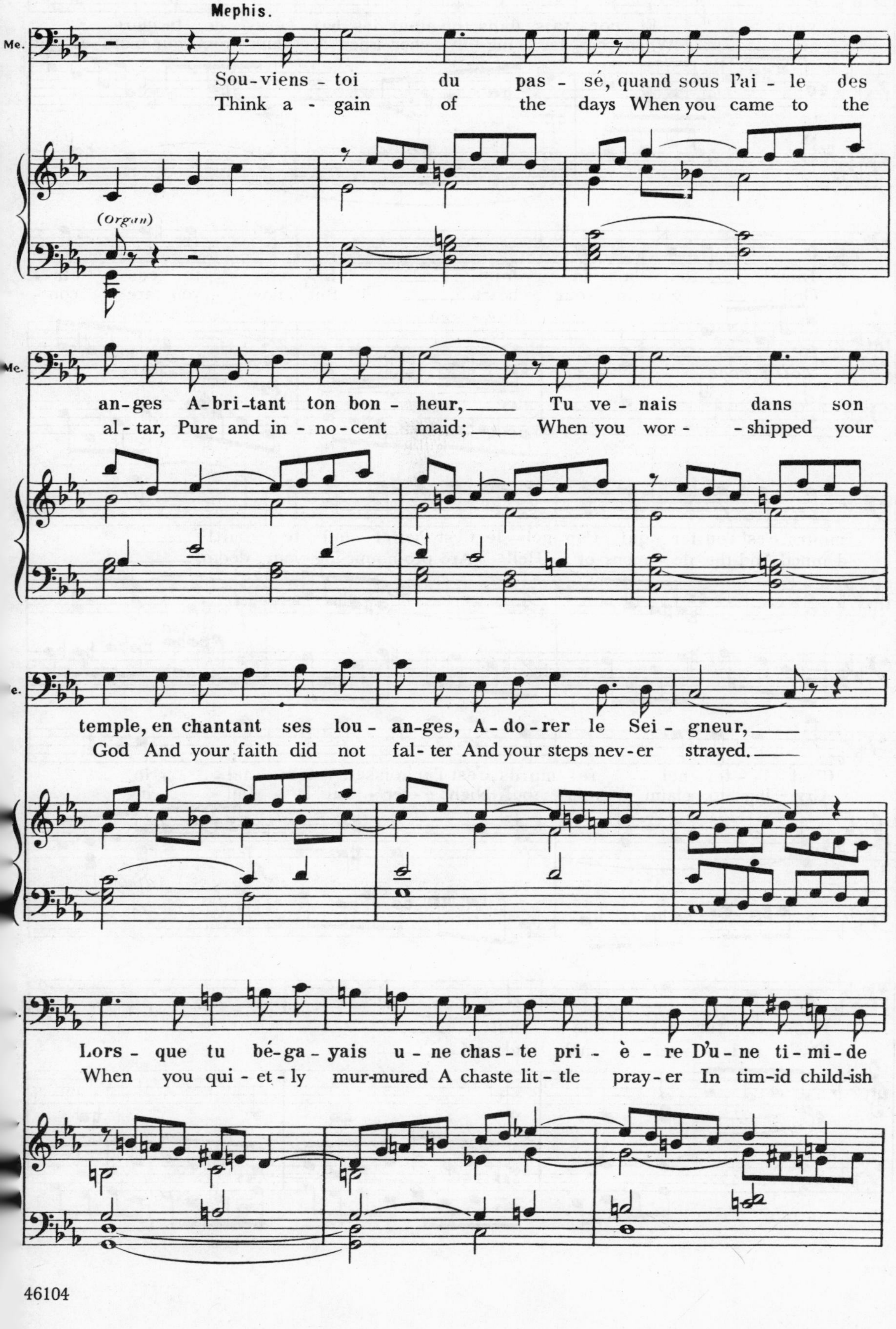
Mephis.
Me.
Sou-viens-toi du pas-sé, quand sous l'ai-le des
Think a-gain of the days When you came to the
(Organ)
an-ges A-bri-tant ton bon-heur, Tu ve-nais dans son
al-tar, Pure and in-no-cent maid; When you wor-shipped your
temple, en chantant ses lou-an-ges, A-do-rer le Sei-gneur,
God And your faith did not fal-ter And your steps nev-er strayed.
Lors-que tu bé-ga-yais u-ne chas-te pri-è-re D'u-ne ti-mi-de
When you qui-et-ly mur-mured A chaste lit-tle pray-er In tim-id child-ish

Me.
voix, Et por- tais dans ton cœur les bai- sers de ta mère, Et
art, When you lov- ing- ly cher-ished A kiss from your moth-er And
Dieu tout à la fois! É- cou- te ces cla-
God was in your heart. But now you are con-
(Orch. & Org.)
colla voce
pp
meurs, c'est l'en-fer qui t'ap-pel- le, C'est l'enfer qui te suit!
demned And the de- mons of Hell Are pro-nounc-ing your doom,
cresc.
C'est l'é- ter- nel re- mords, c'est l'angoisse é- ter- nel- le
Cry- ing to claim your soul. Night e- ter- nal is fall- ing,
f
dim.
Dans l'é- ter- nel- le nuit!
Dark and e- ter- nal gloom!
p

Margarita.
Mg.
Dieu! quelle est cet-te voix qui me par-le dans
God, what voice comes to me From the shad-ows as-
(Orch.)
pp
l'ombre? Dieu tout puissant! Quel voi-le sombre Sur moi des-cend?
cend-ing? Al-might-y God, dark-ness is fall-ing up-on my eyes!
Più mosso.
Chorus of Priests and Boys (invisible)
SOPRANOS, TENORS, BASSES.
ff
Quand du Seigneur le jour lui-ra
When the Judg-ment trum-pets thun-der,
f (Organ)
(Orch.)
Brass
Sa croix au ciel res-plen-di-ra
Then the cross shall shine in splen-dor,
(Organ)
(Orch.)
Et l'u-ni-vers s'é-crou-le-ra!
And the U-ni-verse pass a-way.
(Organ)
(Orch.)

Margarita.
Ma.
Hé-las! hé-las! ce chant pi-eux est plus ter-rible en-
A-las! A-las! Is there no mer-cy in this fear-some
Vlns.
pp
Mephis.
Ma.
Me.
co-re! Non! pour toi Dieu n'a plus de par-
warn-ing? No! For you, no for-give-ness from
f
Me.
don! Pour toi le ciel n'a plus d'au-
God! For you, no day will have a
Me.
ro-re! non! non!
dawn-ing! No! No!
Chorus of Priests, etc. (invisible)
ff
Que di-rai-je a-lors au Sei-gneur,
Who will help me, Who will guide me?
Più mosso.
f (Organ)
(Orch.)
3

Où trou - ve - rai - je un pro - tec - teur,
Who will shield me, Stand be - side me
(Organ)
(Orch.)
Quand l'in - no - cent n'est pas sans peur!
When the blame-less souls too must fear?
(Organ)
(Orch.)
Margarita.
Ma.
Ah! ce chant m'étouffe et m'op - pres - se, Je
Ah, that chant is sti - fling my spir - it, I'm
pp
Ma.
Me.
Mephis.
suis dans un cer - cle de fer! A -
crushed by a strong i - ron band! Fare -
cresc.
f
Me.
dieu les nuits d'a - mour,
well to nights of love,

Me.
et les jours pleins d'i - vres - - se!
to the days of en - chant - - ment!
Me.
à toi mal - heur! à toi l'en -
Your soul is damned! Your soul is
ff
Margarita.
rit.
Più lento.
Ma.
Sei - gneur, Sei - gneur! accueil - lez la pri -
O Lord, O Lord, I im - plore Thee to
Me.
fer!
damned!
SOPRANOS.
Chorus of Priests, etc.
Sei - gneur, Sei -
O Lord, O
TENORS.
Più lento.
(Organ)
p rit.
(Orch.)

è - re Des cœurs mal - heu - reux! Qu'un ra - yon de vo - tre lu -
hear me, O Lord, hear my pray'r! Shed the light of Thy bound-less
gneur! ac - cueil - lez la pri - è - re Des cœurs mal - heu -
Lord, shed the light of Thy mer - cy On those in de -
miè - re Des-cen - de sur eux! Sei - gneur, accueil-lez la pri -
mer - cy On those in de - spair, O Lord, Shed the light of Thy
reux! Des cœurs mal - heu - reux!
spair, On those in de - spair!
Qu'un ra -
Ease the
è - re, la pri - è - re des cœurs mal - heu - reux! Qu'un ra -
mer - cy, of Thy mer - cy On those in de - spair. Ease the
Qu'un ra - yon de vo - tre lu - miè - re Des -
Ease the pain of an-guish and mis - 'ry Of
yon de vo - tre lu - miè - re Des -
pain of an - guish and mis - 'ry, Of

Ma.
yon de vo-tre lu-miè-re, qu'un ra-yon de vo-tre lu-
pain of an-guish and mis-'ry, Ease the pain of an-guish and
cen-de sur eux, des-cen-de sur
those in de-spair, Of those in de-
cen-de sur eux, des-cen-de sur
those in de-spair, Of those in de-
cresc.
Ma.
miè-re Des-cen-de sur eux!
mis-'ry Of those in de-spair!
eux, sur eux!
spair, de-spair!
eux, sur eux!
spair, de-spair!
f
ff
Mephistoph.
Me.
Mar-gue-ri-te,
Mar-ga-ri-ta!

sois mau- di- - te!
Be ac- curs- - ed!
Margarita.
Ah!
Ah!
(He vanishes.)
à toi l'en- fer!
Your soul is damned!
fff
(Organ)
dim.
p
pp

Nº 14. The Soldiers' Chorus.

SCENE 3

Tempo di marcia.

Cornet
Wind
cresc.
f
Ob., Hn., etc.
f
Tutti
ff
f
ff
Ob., Hn., etc.
Tutti

Chorus of Soldiers.
TENORS I.
f
Dé - po - sons les ar - mes, Dé - po - sons les ar - mes, Dans nos fo -
Now the war is o - ver, Now the war is o - ver; Friends, put your
TENORS II.
f
Dé - po - sons les ar - mes, Dé - po - sons les ar - mes, Dans nos fo -
Now the war is o - ver, Now the war is o - ver; Friends, put your
BASSES I & II (Valentine w. B. I).
f
Dé - po - sons les ar - mes, Dé - po - sons les ar - mes, Dans nos fo -
Now the war is o - ver, Now the war is o - ver; Friends, put your
p espress.
yers en - fin nous voi - ci re - ve - nus, Nos mè - res en
swords to rest, We are home once a - gain. You moth - ers, be
p
yers en - fin nous voi - ci re - ve - nus, Nos mè - res en
swords to rest, We are home once a - gain. You moth - ers, be
p
yers en - fin nous voi - ci re - ve - nus, Nos mè - res en
swords to rest, We are home once a - gain. You moth - ers, be
p
lar - mes, Nos mè - res et nos sœurs ne nous at - ten - dront
hap - py, You sweet-hearts, dry your tears, Have done with grief and
lar - mes, Nos mè - res et nos sœurs ne nous at - ten - dront
hap - py, You sweet-hearts, dry your tears, Have done with grief and
lar - mes, Nos mè - res et nos sœurs ne nous at - ten - dront
hap - py, You sweet-hearts, dry your tears, Have done with grief and

plus Déposons les armes, Nos mères en larmes, Nos
pain. No weeping and crying, No mourning and sighing. You
mères et nos sœurs ne nous attendront plus, Nos mères et nos
sweethearts, have no fears, We men are home at last; You mothers, dry your
sœurs ne nous attendront plus.
tears, The time for grief is past.
Fl., Cl., Cornet, etc.
dim.

Vi-
Dé-po-sons les ar-mes,
War and strife are o-ver,
Dé-po-sons les ar-
Now the war is o-
Dé-po-sons les ar-mes,
War and strife are o-ver,
Dé-po-sons les ar-
Now the war is o-
Dé-po-sons les ar-mes,
War and strife are o-ver,
Dé-po-sons les ar-
Now the war is o-
Siebel (embarrassed)
S.
En ef-fet je...
Yes, it's I . . . I . . .
Valentine (noticing Siebel)
Recit.
V.
Eh! parbleu! c'est Sie-bel!
Bless my soul, that's Sie-bel!
Viens
I
mes!
ver!
mes!
ver!
mes!
ver!
Tempo. Allegro moderato.
V.
vi-te, viens dans mes bras!
greet you, dear faith-ful friend.

Recit.
Tempo moderato.
Siebel.
Et Marguerite?
And Mar-ga-ri - ta?
Elle est à l'é - gli - se, je crois...
She still is in church, I be-lieve.
p
Valentine.
Oui, pri-ant Dieu pour moi, Oui, pri-ant Dieu pour
Yes, there she prays for me, Yes, there she prays for
p
più animato
moi! Chè-re sœur! comme el-le va prê-ter une oreille atten-
me. Dear-est child, how she will love To hear all the tales of ad-
più animato
cresc.
Allegro.
ti-ve Au ré-cit de nos com-bats!
ven-ture, How we fought and won the war.
f
f

Chorus.
TENORS I.
Oui, c'est plai-sir dans les fa-
Yes, they will love hear-ing the
TENORS II.
Oui, c'est plai-sir dans les fa-
Yes, they will love hear-ing the
BASSES I. II.
Oui, c'est plai-sir dans les fa-
Yes, they will love hear-ing the
mil - les De conter aux enfants qui fré-missent tout bas,
sto - ry! We will tell ev-'ry-one who comes from near and far
mil - les De conter aux enfants qui fré-missent tout bas,
sto - ry! We will tell ev-'ry-one who comes from near and far
mil - les De conter aux enfants qui fré-missent tout bas,
sto - ry! We will tell ev-'ry-one who comes from near and far
Aux vieillards, aux jeu-nes fil - les, La guerre et ses com-
Tales of brav - 'ry and glo - ry, of brav - 'ry in the
Aux vieillards, aux jeu-nes fil - les, La guerre et ses com-
Tales of brav - 'ry and glo - ry, of brav - 'ry in the
Aux vieillards, aux jeu-nes fil - les, La guerre et ses com-
Tales of brav - 'ry and glo - ry, of brav - 'ry in the
stacc.

bats, La guer - re, la guerre et ses com - bats.
war, of glo - ry and brav - 'ry in the war.
bats, La guer - re, la guerre et ses com - bats.
war, of glo - ry and brav - 'ry in the war.
bats, La guer - re, la guerre et ses com - bats.
war, of glo - ry and brav - 'ry in the war.
ff
=De
Tempo marziale.
ff
Wind, etc.
ff
Chorus.
TENORS.
f
Gloire im - mor - tel - le De nos a - ïeux,
Hail to the he - roes of long a - go,
BASSES.
f
Gloire im - mor - tel - le De nos a - ïeux,
Hail to the he - roes of long a - go,
f

Sois nous fi - dè - le, Mourons comme eux! — Et sous ton
Men who cou - ra-geous-ly met the foe. — We fought like

ai - le, Sol-dats vain-queurs, Di - ri - ge nos pas, di - ri - ge nos pas, en-
you for the cause of right, — Our spir-it is high, our spir-it is high, our

flam - me nos cœurs! — Pour toi, mè - re pa-tri - -
hon - or is bright. — For you, dear na - tive land, —

e, Af-fron-tant le sort, — Tes fils, l'âme aguer - ri - -
Let our ban - ner fly, — At your call and com-mand —

f
e, Ont bra-vé la mort. Ta voix sain-te nous crie:
We will glad- die. Proud and hap-py are we,
f
e, Ont bra-vé la mort. Ta voix sain-te nous crie:
We will glad-ly die. Proud and hap-py are we,
f
En a-vant, sol-dats! Le fer à la main, le fer à la main cou-
We have won the fight, The bat-tle is done, The vic-to-ry won, Our
En a-vant, sol-dats! Le fer à la main, le fer à la main cou-
We have won the fight, The bat-tle is done, The vic-to-ry won, Our
f
pp
rez aux combats! Gloire im-mor-tel-le De nos a-ïeux,
hon-or is bright. Hail to the he-roes of long a-go,
pp
rez aux combats! Gloire im-mor-tel-le De nos a-ïeux,
hon-or is bright. Hail to the he-roes of long a-go,
Tutti
dim.
pp
cresc.
Sois nous fi-dè-le, Mourons comme eux!
Men who cou-ra-geous-ly met the foe.
cresc.
Sois nous fi-dè-le, Mourons comme eux!
Men who cou-ra-geous-ly met the foe.
cresc.
cresc

Et sous ton ai-le, Sol-dats vain-queurs, Di-
We fought like you for the cause of right, Our
ff
ri-ge nos pas, en-flam-me nos cœurs!
spir-its are high, our hon-or is bright.
p
Vers nos fo-yers Hâ-tons le
Now we are home, our du-ty
Cl. Horns etc.
p Saxhorns, Bn. etc.
pas, On nous attend, la paix est fai-te,
done, The time has come for cel-e-bra-tion.
Plus de sou-
Let us re-

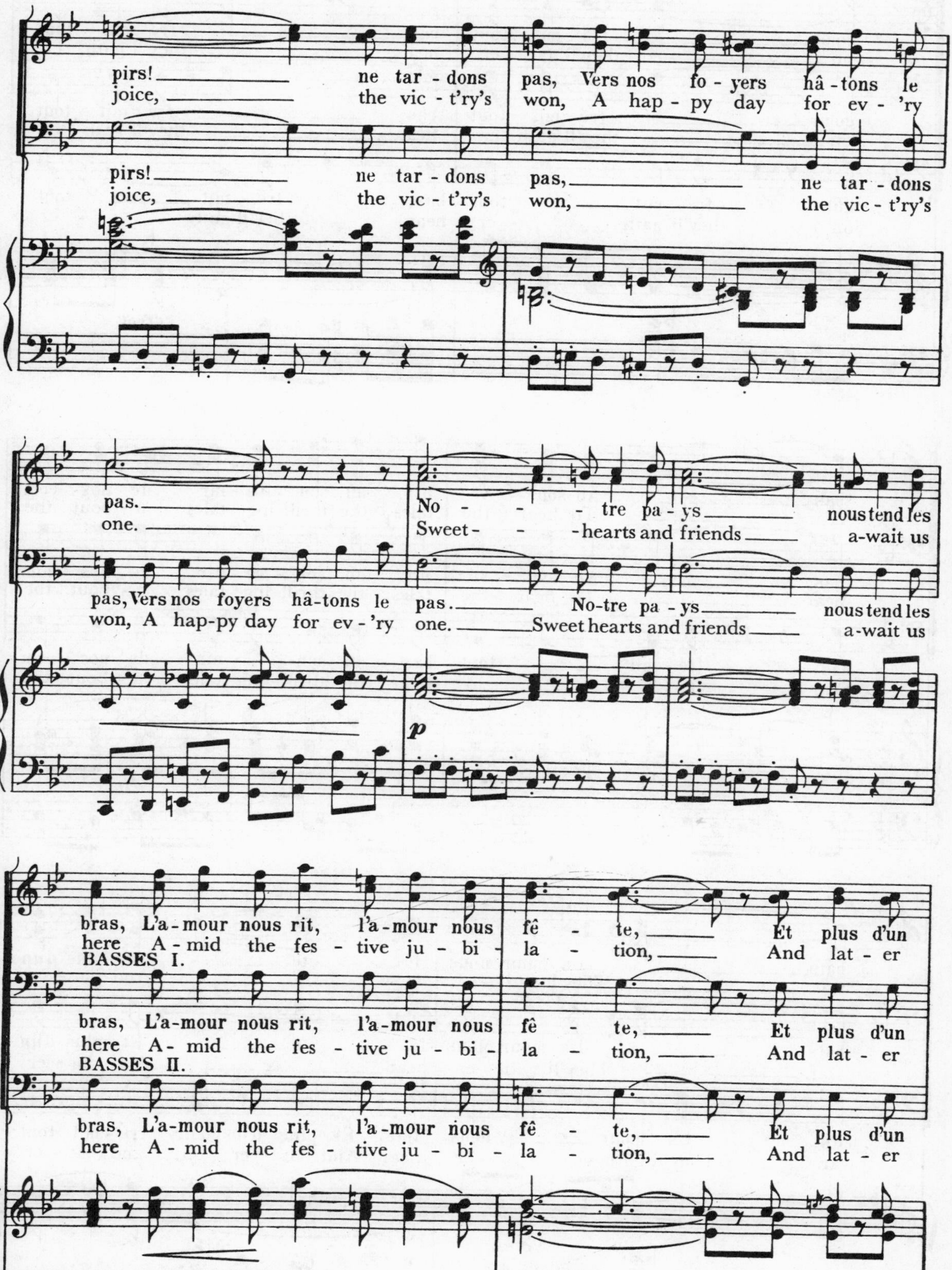

46104

cœur fré - mit tout bas, fré - mit tout
on they'll gath - er near, they'll gath - er
cœur fré - mit tout bas, fré - mit tout
on they'll gath - er near, they'll gath - er
cœur fré - mit tout bas, fré - mit tout
on they'll gath - er near, they'll gath - er
cresc.
dim.
bas Au sou - ve - nir, au sou - ve - nir de nos com-
near To hear the tales, the thrill-ing tales a - bout the
bas Au sou - ve - nir, au sou - ve - nir de nos com-
near To hear the tales, the thrill-ing tales a - bout the
bas, fré - mit tout bas au sou - ve - nir de nos com-
near To hear, to hear the thrill-ing tales a - bout the
dim.
p
cresc.
bats, L'a-mour nous fê - te, Et plus d'un
war. They'll gath - er near, And lat - er
bats, L'a-mour nous fê - te, Et plus d'un
war. They'll gath - er near, And lat - er
bats, L'a - mour nous fête, Et plus d'un cœur fré - mit tout
war. They'll gath - er near, And lat - er on, and lat - er
cresc.

f
dim.
cœur fré-mit tout bas, fre-mit tout bas Au sou-ve-nir de nos com-
on they'll gath-er near to hear the tales, the thrill-ing tales a-bout the
cœur fré-mit tout bas, fré-mit tout bas Au sou-ve-nir de nos com-
on they'll gath-er near to hear the tales, the thrill-ing tales a-bout the
bas, fré-mit tout bas, fré-mit tout bas Au sou-ve-nir de nos com-
on they'll gath-er near to hear the tales, the thrill-ing tales a-bout the
p
molto cresc.
bats. Hâ-tons le pas, Ne tar-dons
war. We're com-ing home, The war is
BASSES I. II.
bats. Hâ-tons le pas, Ne tar-dons
war. We're com-ing home, The war is
Vlns.
pas, Hâ-tons le pas, Ne tar-dons pas.
won, our du-ty's done, we're com-ing home!
pas, Hâ-tons le pas, Ne tar-dons pas.
won, our du-ty's done, we're com-ing home!

ff
Gloire im-mor-tel-le De nos a-ïeux,— Sois nous fi-dè-le, Mourons comme eux!— Et sous ton ai-le, Sol-dats vain-queurs,— Di-ri-ge nos pas, en-flam-me nos cœurs! Di-ri-ge nos pas,— en-flam-me nos
Hail to the he-roes of long a-go,— Men who cou-rageous-ly met the foe.— We fought like you for the cause of right,— Our spir-it is high, our hon-or is bright. Our spir-it is high,— our hon-or is
ff
Gloire im-mor-tel-le De nos a-ïeux,— Sois nous fi-dè-le, Mou-rons comme eux!— Et sous ton ai-le, Sol-dats vain-queurs,— Di-ri-ge nos pas, en-flam-me nos cœurs! Di-ri-ge nos pas, di-ri-ge nos pas,— en-flam-me nos
Hail to the he-roes of long a-go,— Men who cou-rageous-ly met the foe.— We fought like you for the cause of right,— Our spir-it is high, our hon-or is bright. Our spir-it is high, our spir-it is high,— our hon-or is
ff

cœurs! Di-ri-ge nos pas, di-ri-ge nos
bright. Our spir-it is high, our spir-it is
cœurs! Di-ri-ge nos pas, di-ri-ge nos pas, di-ri-ge nos
bright. Our spir-it is high, our spir-it is high, our spir-it is
rit.
a tempo
pas, en-flam-me nos cœurs!
high, our hon-or is bright.
rit.
pas, en-flam-me nos cœurs!
high, our hon-or is bright.
rit.
a tempo

(The soldiers march off. Valentine and Siebel remain.)
Cornet
Wind
mf
cresc.
dim.
p
pp
perdendosi

Recit.
Moderato.
Valentine.
V.
Al-lons, Sie-bel, en-trons dans la mai-
And now, Sie-bel, we'll go in-to the
Piano.
f
son! Le verre en main, tu me fe-ras rai-son!
house. Let's drink a toast, This is a hap-py day.
Siebel. Recit.
Non... n'en-tre pas!
No, don't go in.
Allegro.
Pour-quoi?.. tu dé-tour-nes la tê-te...
Why not? Is there some-thing the mat-ter?
fp
Ton re-gard fuit le mien... Sie-bel... Ex-pli-que-toi?
You're a-void-ing my eyes.— Sie-bel, will you ex-plain?
cresc.
ff

S.
Siebel (with an effort)
Eh bien!... non, je ne puis!
It's just... No... no, I can't...
V.
(starts toward the house)
Ar-
I
Que veux-tu di-re?
Why can't you tell me?
Oboe
Va.
rê-te! sois clé-ment, Va-len-tin!
beg you, have pit-y on her!
(He tries to hold Valentine back.)
Par-don-ne-
Val-en-tine,
Laisse-moi, lais-se-moi!
Let me go, let me go!
(rushes into the house.)
Clar.
Bn.
lui! Mon Dieu! je vous im-plo-re! Mon
don't! Oh please, let me im-plore you! Dear
Dieu, pro-té-gez la!
God, save her from harm!

Nº 15. Scene and Serenade.

sence ail-leurs se-rait bien mieux fê - té - e! Le sab-bat nous at
get, our pres-ence is de-mand-ed else - where, At Wal-pur - gis

tend! Mar-gue - ri-te! Je vois que mes a-vis sont vains et que l'a-
Night. Mar-ga - ri-ta! I see you will not lis-ten To the warn-ing

mour l'em-por - te!.. Mais, pour vous faire ou-vrir la
voice of cau - tion. But if you wish the door to

por-te, Vous a-vez grand be - soin du secours de ma voix.
o-pen, My ser-en-ade will do it In no time at all.

(Faust, deep in thought, moves away.)
Fl., Ob. & Clar.
poco meno mosso
f
Vlns.
p
Mephistopheles. (accompanying himself on the guitar)
Me.
Vous qui fai - tes l'en - dor - mi - e, N'en - ten - dez - vous pas,
Can it be that you are sleep - ing Or do you pre - tend,
N'en - ten - dez - vous pas, Ô Ca - the - ri - ne, ma mi - e, N'en - ten - dez - vous
Or do you pre - tend? Ca - the - ri - na, hear my sing - ing, Don't you know your
pas Ma voix et mes pas? Ain - si ton ga - lant t'ap -
friend, Don't you know your friend? Do not let your lov - er
pel - le, Ain - si ton ga - lant t'ap - pel - le,
lin - ger, Do not let your lov - er lin - ger,

riten.
a tempo
Et ton cœur l'en croit. Ah! ah! ah! ah! ah! ah! ah! ah! ah!
Lend a friend-ly ear. Ha ha ha ha ha ha ha ha ha
a tempo
riten.
ah! N'ouvre ta por-te, ma bel-le, Que la bague au
ha! Till the ring is on your fin-ger, Lock your door, my
Vlns.
Vcl.
doigt, N'ou-vre ta por-te, ma bel-le, Que la bague au
dear! Till the ring is on your fin-ger, Lock your door, my
cresc.
doigt, Que la bague au doigt!
dear, Lock your door, my dear!
Ca-the-ri-ne que j'a-
Ca-the-ri-na, I im-
poco meno mosso
stacc.
Vlns.

Me.
do - re, Pourquoi re - fu - ser, Pour - quoi re - fu - ser
plore you, Give your love to me, Give your love to me!
Fl. & Ob.
A l'a - mant qui vous im - plo - re, Pourquoi re - fu - ser Un si doux bai -
For you know that I a - dore you, Hear my fer - vent plea, Hear my fer - vent
dim.
ser?
plea.
Vlns.
Ain - si ton ga - lant sup - pli - e,
It's your gal - lant lov - er sing - ing,
Ob.
Ain - si ton ga - lant sup - pli - e,
It's your gal - lant lov - er sing - ing
riten.
Et ton cœur l'en
At your win - dow
a tempo
f
p
croit. Ah! ah! ah! ah! ah! ah! ah! ah! ah! ah!
here. Ha! ha! ha! ha! ha! ha! ha! ha! ha! ha!
a tempo f
pp
p

Me.
Ne donne un bai - ser, ma mi - e, Que la bague au — doigt, — Ne —
Till the wed-ding bells are ring - ing, Lock your door, — dear! — Till —
cresc.
— donne un bai - ser, ma mi - e, Que la bague au doigt. Que la bague au
— the wed-ding bells are ring-ing, Lock your door, my dear, Lock your door, my
ad lib.
f
doigt! Ah! ah! ah! ah! ah! ah! ah! ah! ah! ah! ah! ah! ah! ah!
dear! Ha! ha! ha! ha! ha! ha! ha! ha! ha! ha! ha! ha! ha! ha!
f
Presto.
ff

No 16. Trio. The Duel.

Faust. (aside) (Valentine shatters Mephistopheles' guitar.)
Meph.
V.
F.
Me.
rait mieux que moi, je le sais! Sa sœur!.. Quel-le mou - che vous
mind it at all, That I know. His sis - ter! What's the bee in your
Vla.
pp
Vcl.
Me.
V.
Valentine.
pi - que?.. Vous n'aimez donc pas la mu - si - que? As-sez d'ou-
bon-net? Or don't you ap-prove of my son-net? How dare you
f
V.
tra - ge!.. as - sez! A qui de vous dois - je demander
mock me? E - nough! Which one of you will ren-der sat-is-
Vla.
Vcl.
V.
comp - te De mon mal - heur, et de ma hon - te?.. Qui de vous
fac - tion For my dis - grace and my dis - hon - or? Which one of
(Faust draws.)
Mephistopheles.
V.
Me.
deux doit tomber sous mes coups? Vous le vou - lez?.. al-
you must be killed by my sword? Shall we be - gin? Then

lons, doc - teur, al - lons, à
draw, Doc - tor, Ad - vance, at -
Faust. (aside)
Ter - ri - ble et fré - missant,
O ruth-less deed, to shed his blood,
Valentine.
Re - double, ô Dieu puis - sant! ma
O Lord, pro - tect me now, My
vous! De son air me - na - çant, De
tack! At his wrath I can laugh, How
ff
dim.
p
Il gla - ce mon cou - ra - ge! Ter - ri - ble
When I am the of - fend - er! I shud - der
force et mon cou - ra - ge! Re - dou - ble, re -
hon - or's just de - fend - er. Pro - tect me, pro -
son a - veu - gle ra - ge, De son air me - na -
boast - ful a de - fend - er! At his wrath I can

F.
et fré - missant,
Il gla - ce mon cou -
at such a deed
A - gainst a just de -
V.
dou - ble ma force et mon cou -
tect me, My hon - or's just de -
Me.
çant,
De son a - veu - gle ra - ge,
laugh,
How boast - ful a de - fend - er!
F.
ra - ge! Dois - je ver - ser le sang Du
fend - er. Must I now shed his blood When
V.
ra - ge! Per - mets que dans son sang Je
fend - er. My Lord, al - low my arm To
Me.
Moi, je ris! Mon bras puis - sant Va dé - tour -
I can laugh, My force - ful arm shall be His
cresc.

F.
frè - re que j'outra - - ge, Dois - je ver - ser le
I am the of-fend - - er? Must I now shed his
V.
la - ve mon outra - - ge, Dieu puis - sant, Dieu puis -
slay the vile of-fend - - er, That I may shed his
Me.
ner l'o - ra - - ge, Mon bras puis - sant, mon
best de - fend - - er. My force - ful arm shall
f dim. p cresc.
rit. molto a tempo
F.
sang, ver-ser le sang du - frè - re que j'ou - tra - ge?
blood, his guilt-less blood When I am the of - fend - er?
V.
sant! re - double mon cou - ra - ge!
blood, The blood of the of - fend - er.
Me.
bras va détourner l'o - ra - ge.
be His best de - fend - er.
rit. molto a tempo ff
Valentine (grasping the medal which is hanging around his neck)
V.
Et
And
p

V.
toi qui pré-ser-vas mes jours, Toi qui me
you, the trea-sured med-al I wore, Once cher-ished
V.
viens de Mar-gue-ri-te, Je ne veux plus de ton se-cours, Je ne veux
gift of Mar-ga-ri-ta, I do not want you an-y-more, I do not
V.
plus de ton se-cours, Mé-dail-le mau-
want you an-y-more! Ac-curs-ed me-
cresc.
V.
di-te! Je ne veux plus de ton se-cours!
dal-lion, I spurn your help for-ev-er-more.
(He throws the medal away.)
Me.
Mephistopheles (aside)
Tu t'en re-pen-ti-
There you are ver-y
f
fp
Ob. & Cl.

Faust.
Valentine.
F.
V.
Me.
Ter - ri -
O ruth-less
Re - double, ô
O Lord, pro -
ras, tu t'en re - pen - - - ti - ras! De son
wrong, There you are ver - - - y wrong! At his
Vlns.
cresc.
molto f
dim.
ble et fré - mis-sant, Il gla - ce mon cou -
deed, to shed his blood When I am the of -
Dieu puis - sant, ma force et mon cou -
tect me now, My hon - or's just de -
air me - naçant, De son a - veu - gle
wrath I can laugh, How boast - ful a - de -
p
ra - - - ge! Ter - ri - ble
fend - - - er! I shud - der
ra - - - ge! Re - dou - ble, re -
fend - - - er. Pro - tect me, pro -
ra - - - ge, De son air me - na -
fend - - - er! At his wrath I can

F.
et fré - mis - sant
at such a deed
Il gla - ce mon cou -
A - gainst a just de -
V.
dou - ble ma force et mon cou -
tect me, My hon - or's just de -
Me.
çant, de son a - veu - gle ra - ge,
laugh, How boast - ful a de - fend - er!
F.
ra - ge!
fend - er.
Dois - je ver
Must I now
V.
ra - ge!
fend - er.
Per - mets que
My Lord, al -
Me.
Moi, je ris!
I can laugh,
Mon bras puis -
My force - ful
cresc.
F.
ser le sang Du frè - re que j'outra - ge, Dois -
shed his blood When I am the of - fend - er? Must
V.
dans son sang Je la - ve mon outra - ge, Dieu puis -
low my arm To slay the vile of - fend - er, That I
Me.
sant Va dé - tour - ner l'o - ra - ge, Mon
arm shall be his best de - fend - er. My
f
dim.
p
cresc.

rit. molto
a tempo
je ver - ser le sang, ver - ser - le - sang du - frè - re que jou -
I now shed his blood, his — guilt - less — blood When I am the of -
sant, — Dieu puissant! re - dou - ble mon cou -
may — shed his blood, The — blood of the of -
bras puis - sant, mon bras va — dé - tourner l'o -
force - ful arm shall be His — best — de -
rit. molto
a tempo
tra - ge?
fend - er?
ra - ge!
fend - er.
ra - ge!
fend - er.
ff
Valentine.
En gar - de, et dé - fends - toi!
On guard now! Fight to the death!
Meph.
(softly to Faust)
Ser - rez - vous contre
I shall stay be - hind
ff
p

Me.
moi Et poussez seu-le-ment, cher docteur, moi, je pa-
you, And what-ev-er he does on-ly thrust, I will par-
(Valentine engages.)
Me.
re.
ry.
(1st thrust)
ff
fp
(2nd thrust)
ff
fp
(3rd thrust)
ff
(4th thrust)
Valentine (falls, mortally wounded)
Mephistopheles.
V.
Me.
Ah!
Ah!
Voi-ci no-tre hé-ros é-ten-du sur le
Here lies our he-ro beat-en and mor-tal-ly
Tempo moderato.
ff
Horn
p
(He drags Faust away.)
Me.
sa-ble! Au lar-ge maintenant, au lar-ge!
wound-ed! A-way from here! To safe-ty!
cresc.

No 17. The Death of Valentine.

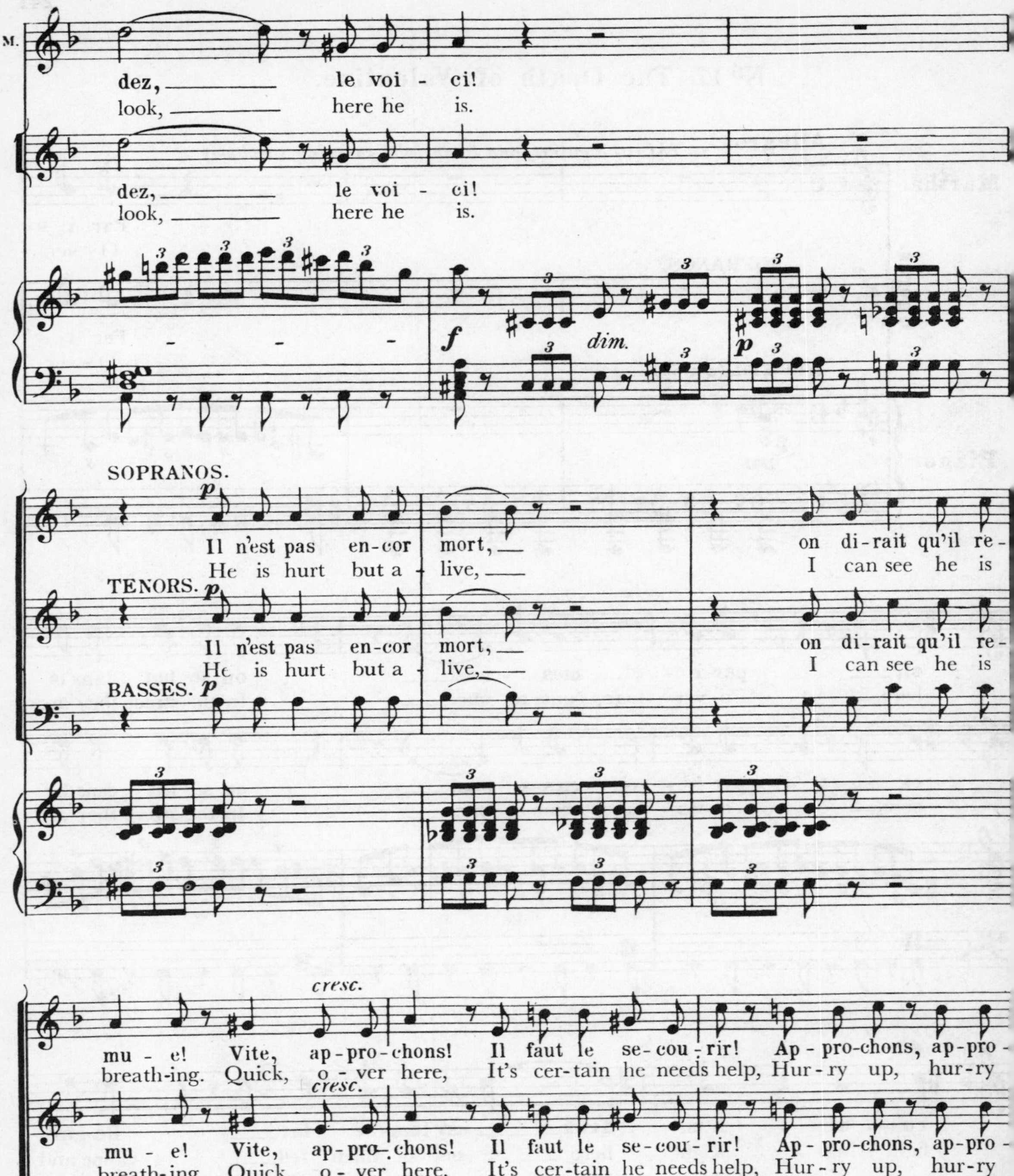

242

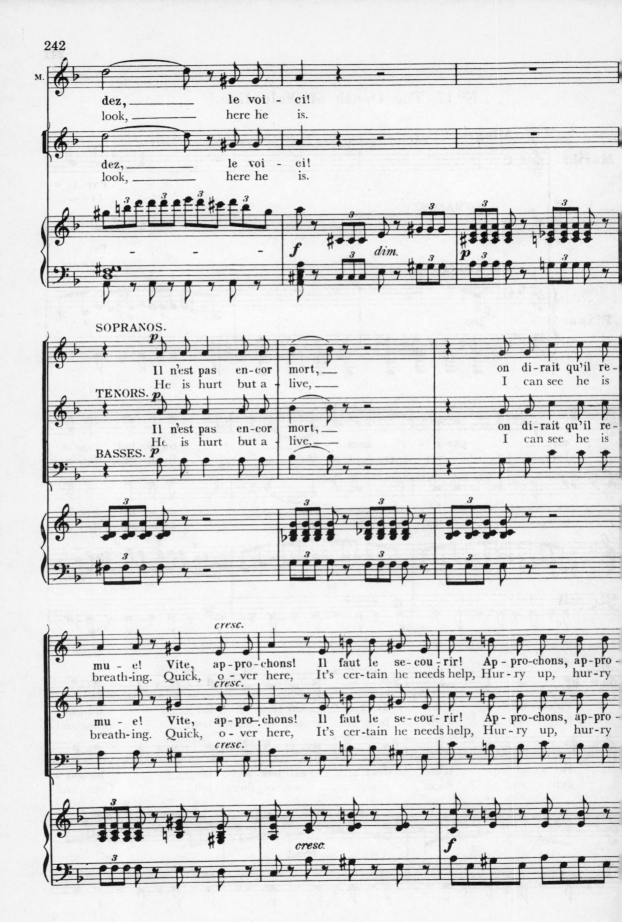

Valentine. (raises himself with an effort)
Mer - ci! mer - ci! De vos
Have done, have done! Do not
chons, Il faut le se - cou - rir!
up, we have to give him help.
chons, Il faut le se - cou - rir!
up, we have to give him help.
Vlns.
p
un poco ritenuto
plain - tes fai - tes-moi grâ - ce! J'ai vu, mor-bleu! la
weep for me an - y long - er. Too of - ten on the
Cl. & Bssn.
tr
sfz
mort en fa - ce Trop sou - vent pour en a - voir
bat - tle - field Have I faced death calm and un - a -
dim.
p
Margarita (appears at back, with Siebel)
Valentine.
peur! Va - len - tin! Va - len - tin! Mar - gue -
fraid. Val - en - tine! Val - en - tine! Mar - ga -
pp
cresc.

(Margarita pushes through the crowd and kneels beside Valentine)
(He pushes her away.)
Margarita.
V. Ma.
ri - te, ma sœur, Que me veux - tu? va t'en! Ô
ri - ta! It's you! Why are you here? Be gone! O
Dieu!
God!
Valentine.
V.
Je meurs par el - le! J'ai sot - te - ment Cher - ché que - relle À son a -
Through her I am dy - ing. It was her lov - er's sword which dealt the mor - tal
sfz
p
Andante.
mant!
blow!
SOPRANOS.
pp
Son a -
Her lov - er's
TENORS.
BASSES.
Chorus.
Andante.
pp
Trombones

Margarita.
Dou -
O
Siebel. (to Valentine)
Grâ - ce!
Spare her!
grâ - ce!
Spare her!
mant!
sword!
mant!
sword!
Vlns.
cresc.
leur cru - el - le! Ô châ - ti -
end - - less sor - row! O bit - ter
grâ - ce pour el - le! grâ - ce!
Spare her the sor - row! Spare her!
Il meurt pour el - le! Il
He fought her lov - er! His
Il meurt pour el - le! Il
He fought her lov - er! His

Ma.
ment! Ô châ - ti - ment!
woe! O bit - ter woe!
S.
grâ - ce! So - yez clé - ment!
Spare her! Her bit - ter woe!
meurt frap - pé par son a - mant!
sword has dealt the mor - tal blow!
meurt frap - pé par son a - mant!
sword has dealt the mor - tal blow!
cresc.
p
Horn
Valentine.
V.
É - cou - te - moi bien, Mar - gue - ri - te:
Now hark to my words, Mar - ga - ri - ta!
V.
Ce qui doit ar - ri - ver, ar - rive à l'heu - re
All which must come to pass Has one ap - point - ed
Brass
p

dite! La mort nous frap-pe quand il faut, Et cha-cun o-bé-
hour. And when the time has come to die, Ev-'ry-one must o-
it aux vo-lon-tés d'en haut! Toi!
bey, Yield-ing to God on high! You!
cresc.
f
dim.
te voi-là dans la mau-vai-se voi-e, Tes blanches
You have strayed on the path of e-vil, What you have
dim.
p
mains ne tra-vail-le-ront plus! Tu re-nie-ras, pour vi-vre dans la
done You can nev-er un-do. So you may live a life of sin-ful
cresc.
joi-e, Tous les de-voirs et tou-tes les ver-
plea-sure, You have de-nied all that is good and
dim.

V.
tus! Va! la hon-te t'ac-
true. Go! May shame o-ver-
cresc.
ff p
V.
ca-ble! Le re-mords suit tes pas! Mais en-fin l'heu-re
whelm you And re-morse tear your heart Un-til death comes to
f p
V.
son-ne! Meurs! et si Dieu te par-
claim you. Die! And though God may for-
f
V.
don-ne, Sois mau-dite i-ci-bas! Si Dieu te par-
give you, Be ac-cursed while you live! Though God may for-
p
V.
don-ne, Si Dieu te par-don-ne, Sois mau-di-te i-ci-
give you, though God may for-give you, Be ac-cursed while you
f

V.
bas!
live!
SOPRANOS.
Ô ter - reur! ô blas - phè - me, À ton
Dread-ful curse! Un - re - lent - ing! Will you
TENORS.
Ô ter - reur! ô blas - phè - me, À ton
Dread-ful curse! Un - re - lent - ing! Will you
BASSES.
Chorus.
dim.
heu - re su - prê - me, in - for - tu -
die un - re - pent - ing? Pray and for -
cresc.
dim.

p
cresc.
p cresc. molto
né,
in - for - tu - né, Songe, hé -
give!
Pray and for - give! You will
p
cresc.
p cresc. molto
né,
in - for - tu - né, Songe, hé -
give!
Pray and for - give! You will
p
cresc.
p
cresc. molto
p
f
p
ff
las! à toi - mê - me: Par - don - ne, si tu
soon meet your Mak - er, for - give her, As you
ff
las! à toi - mê - me: Par - don - ne, si tu
soon meet your Mak - er, for - give her, As you
ff
cresc. molto
ff

dim.
veux être un jour par - don - né!
beg God's for - give - ness to - day.
dim.
veux être un jour par - don - né!
beg God's for - give - ness to - day.
dim.
dim.
p
Valentine.
Mar - gue - ri - te,
Sois mau -
Mar - ga - ri - ta,
be ac -
cresc.
di - te!
La mort t'at - tend
curs - ed!
You, too, will lie
Horns
f
dim.
pp
sur ton gra - bat!
Moi...
je meurs de ta main...
et je
dead in your grave.
I...
I die by your hand
As a
pp

(He dies.)
V.
tombe en sol - dat.
sol - dier and brave.
pp
Più lento d'adagio.
SOPRANOS.
p
pp
Que le Sei-gneur ait son âme et par-donne au pê - cheur.
May God have mer-cy on him and his soul And for - give.
TENORS.
Que le Sei-gneur ait son âme et par-donne au pê - cheur.
May God have mer-cy on him and his soul And for - give.
BASSES.
Più lento d'adagio.
Tempo I.
Clar.
Fl. & Ob.
Clar.
pp

End of Act III.

Act IV.

Nº 18. The Walpurgis Night.

SCENE 1

Allegro. (♩. = 104)
Piano.
ff
(♩. = 96)
pp leggïero
Chorus.
SOPRANOS.
p
Dans les bru - yè - res, Dans les ro - seaux, Par - mi les pier - res
O - ver the heath - er, Marsh - es, mead - ows, Light as a feath - er,
pp e leggiero

Et sur les eaux, De place en pla - ce, Per - çant la nuit,
Ee - rie shad - ows, Air - i - ly flash - ing Low - er, high - er,
S'al - lume et pas - se Un feu qui luit. A - lerte, a -
Flam - ing and flash - ing, Glow - ing fire, They float, they
ler - te! De loin, de près, Dans l'her - be
hov - er, Be - low, a - bove, In fields of
ver - te, Sous les cy - près, Mou - van - tes
clo - ver, In wood and grove, Flames burn - ing
flam - mes, Ra - yons gla - cés, Ce sont les
bright - ly, Rays blaz - ing red, Souls drift - ing
p
p

pp
â - mes Des tré - pas - sés, Ce
light - ly, Souls of the dead, Souls
p
p
pp
sont les â - - mes Des tré - pas - sés,
drift - ing light - - ly, Souls of the dead,
Ce sont les â - mes Des tré - pas - sés.
Souls drift - ing light - ly, Souls of the dead.

Allegro.
p
poco a poco cresc.
f

Faust.
Recit.
Ar - rê - te!
No far - ther!
fp
Où som-mes - nous?
Where are we now?
Mephistopheles.
N'as-tu pas pro-mis De m'ac-com-pa-gner sans rien di - re?
You gave me your word not to speak to me on our jour-ney.
fp
fp
fp
Maestoso.
misurato
Dans mon em - pi - re! I - ci, doc-teur, tout m'est sou - mis! Voi - ci la nuit de Wal - pur -
This is my king-dom, And here, my friend, I reign su - preme. It's time to start Wal - pur - gis
Maestoso.
f
p
p

Me.
gis.
Night!
SOPRANOS.
p sombre
Voi - ci la nuit de Wal - pur - - gis.
It's time to start Wal - pur - gis Night.
TENORS.
p sombre
Voi - ci la nuit de Wal - pur - - gis.
It's time to start Wal - pur - gis Night!
BASSES.
p sombre
Chorus.
Allegro.
Allegro.
cresc.
ff
ff
Hou, hou, hou, hou, hou, hou, hou,
Hoo hoo, hoo hoo, hoo hoo, hoo
ff
Hou, hou, hou, hou, hou, hou, hou,
Hoo hoo, hoo hoo, hoo hoo, hoo
ff

Faust.
Recit.
Mon sang se gla - ce!
My blood is fro - zen!
Mephistopheles.
At -
Be -
hou!
hoo!
hou!
hoo!
Recit.
fp
fp
Adagio.
tends! je n'ai qu'un signe à fai - re, Pour qu'i - ci tout change et s'é -
hold! As soon as I com - mand it, All the dark-ness will change in-to
Adagio.
f
p
clai - re!
splen - dor!
Tam - tam
ff

Andante maestoso.
Piano.
pp
cresc.
f
dim.
p
Mcphistopheles.
Me.
Jus-qu'aux premiers feux du ma-tin, À l'a-bri des re-gards pro-
Till the morn-ing glows in the sky, Hid-den far from pro-fane mor-tal
Me.
fa - nes, Je t'offre u-ne pla-ce au fes-tin Des rei-nes et des
glanc - es, As my guest of hon-or You shall feast with he - ro-ines of
cresc.
colla voce

cour - ti - sa - - nes.
great_ ro - manc - - es.
Maestoso assai.
ff
Ped.
Chorus.
SOPRANOS.
f
Que les cou - pes s'em - plis - sent, Au
As_ the_ wine flows a - bound - ing The
nom des an - ciens dieux, Que les airs re - ten -
an - cient_ gods we hail, Joy - ous songs are re -

tis - sent De nos ac-cords jo-yeux.
sound - ing Till the sky grows pale.
Mephistopheles.
Me.
Rei - nes de beau-té De l'an-ti-qui -
Beau - ties we a-dore, Queens from days of
té, Clé - o - pâtre au doux yeux, La -
yore, Cle - o - pa - tra fair as day, Tha -
ïs au front char-mant, Lais-sez-nous, lais - sez -
ïs, in bright ar-ray. Let us all take our
p

nous au ban-quet pren-dre place un mo - ment.
place At the rev-el and ca-rouse while we may.

(to Faust)

Al - lons! al - lons! pour gué-rir la
And you, my friend, this will heal Your

fié-vre De ton cœur bles - sé, Prends cet - te
love-strick-en heart at last. Come, take this

Tempo I.

cou - pe, et que ta lèvre Y pui-se l'ou-bli du pas - sé!
gob - let, Drink deep-ly and you soon will for-get the drear-y past.

Chorus.

SOPRANOS I & II.

colla voce

Tempo I.

Que les
As the

*) The Ballet added for the Grand Opéra begins with this measure. (See Appendix.)

F.
bli - e! Donne et bu - vons, bu - vons jus-qu'à la
sor - row. Come, let us sing and drink till to-
f
rit.
Allegro moderato.
F.
li - e, donne et bu - vons, bu - vons jus-qu'à la li - e!
mor - row, Come, let us sing and drink un - til to - mor - row.
rit.
ff
p
Faust.
F.
Doux nec - tar, dans ton i - vres - se Tiens mon cœur en - se - ve -
Gold - en nec - tar, brew that bless - es, Soothe my heart in tran - quil
Chorus.
SOPRANOS.
f
Ô doux nec -
O soothe my
cresc.
dim.

F.
li, Qu'un bai - ser de feu ca - res - se Jus - qu'au jour mon front _ pâ -
bliss, Show - er me with warm ca - ress - es, On my brow be - stow — your
tar!
heart,
Ô doux _ nec -
O soothe — my
p
dim.
F.
li. _ En - dors _ dans ton i - vres - se _ Mon
kiss! _ Be - stow _ your heal - ing grac - es _ To
tar!
heart.
F.
coeur _ en - se - ve - li! _
dim _ my heart's re - gret, _
Dans la
In your
Ô _ doux nec - tar!
Have _ no re - gret!
cresc. molto
f

rit.
a tempo
Mephis.
F.
Me.
coupe en-chan-te-res-se Pour ja-mais je bois l'ou-bli! Dans la
ten-der warm em-brac-es, Mag-ic cup, let me for-get! In your
ff
Dans la
In your
f
colla voce
ff
Faust.
p
Vo-lup-
Joy-ous
coupe en-chan-te-res-se Pour ja-mais bu-vons l'ou-bli!
ten-der warm em-brac-es, Mag-ic cup, let us for-get!
coupe en-chan-te-res-se Pour ja-mais bu-vons l'ou-bli!
ten-der warm em-brac-es, Mag-ic cup, let us for-get!
3
p
té, de-vant tes char-mes Se ré-veil-le le dé-
love, your charms ex-cite me And a-wak-en my de-
ff
Ô vo-lup-
God-dess of
f

F.
sir, Lais - se - nous loin des a - lar - mes Au pas -
sire, How you beck - on and in - vite me, Set my
té!
joy!
cresc.
sa - ge te sai - sir! Dé - es - se, par tes
sens - es all a - fire! O God - dess, with your
ff
Ô vo - lup - té!
God - dess of joy!
f
dim.
p
char - mes Ré - veil - le le dé - sir,
grac - es, En - chant my heart to - night.
ff
Ô
God -
cresc. molto

rit.
Et no - yons l'a-mour en lar-mes Dans l'i - vresse et le plai -
Drown the past in your em-brac-es, In an or - gy of de -
vo - lup - té!
- dess of joy!
f colla voce
sir!
light!
Mephistopheles.
Et no - yons l'a-mour en lar-mes Dans la joie et le plai -
Drown the past in your em - brac-es, In an or - gy of de -
ff
Et no - yons l'a - mour en lar-mes Dans la joie et le plai -
Drown the past in your em-brac-es, In an or - gy of de -
ff
sir!
light!
sir!
light!
*) Andantino.
dolce
pp

*) The Ballet ends on this measure.

Mephistopheles.
Me.
Que ton i - vres - se, ô vo - lup -
May your en - chant - ment, God - dess of
té, É - touf - fe le re - mords dans son
love, Ex - tin - guish all re - morse in his
cœur en - chan - té! Ô vo - lup - té, vo - lup -
poor love - lorn heart! God - dess of love, joy - ous
té, que ton i - vresse é - touf - fe les re - mords dans son cœur en - chan -
love, with mag - ic charm ex - tin - guish all re - morse in his poor love - lorn
cresc.
f

Allegro.
Me.
té!
heart!
8
Piano.
fff
(Faust sees a vision of Margarita.)
8
Mephistoph.
Qu'as-tu donc?
Have you gone mad?
fp
Faust.
Ne la vois-tu pas,
Don't you see her there,
là... devant nous, muette et blê-me?.. Quel étrange or-ne-
there... Before our eyes so pale and si-lent? What a strange thing she
pp

Meph. Vision!
(spoken) A vision!
F.
ment au-tour de ce beau cou! Un ru-ban rou - ge qu'el-le
wears A-round her slen-der throat! A scar-let rib - bon that she's
Meph. Magie!!
(spoken) Magic!
ca - che! Un ru-ban rouge, é-troit comme un tranchant de
hid - ing! A scar-let rib-bon there, thin as the edge of an
cresc.
Meph. Sortilège!
(spoken) Witchcraft!
ha - che! Mar-gue-ri-te! je sens se dres-ser mes che -
axe blade! Mar-ga-ri-ta! I can't bear the hor-ri-ble
ff
f
veux! Je veux la voir! viens! je le
sight! Lead me to her! Come! I com -

Allegro.
F
veux!
mand!
ff
fff
8
8

Nº 19. Final Trio.

Prison Scene.

SCENE 2

Fl.
cresc.
dim.
Clar.
p
(Curtain rises.)
a piacere
ff
dim.
p
Allegro.
Vlns.
f
dim.
p

cresc.
Fl., Ob., etc.
f
(Margarita asleep)
(Faust and Mephistopheles enter.)

Faust (to Mephistopheles)
Va t'en!
A-way!
Mephistopheles.
Moderato.
Le jour va lui-re; on dresse l'é-cha-faud,
The day is dawn-ing; The scaf-fold is pre-pared,
p Cornets etc.
Dé-ci-de sans re-tard Mar-gue-rite a te sui-vre
You must at once per-suade Mar-ga-ri-ta to join you.
mf
Le geô-lier dort,
The guard's a-sleep,
pp
Faust.
Lais-se-
Leave us a-
voi-ci les clefs, il faut que ta main d'homme la dé-li-vre.
I have his key, Your hu-man hand is need-ed to free her.

Adagio.
F.
nous!
lone!
Me.
Hâ - te - toi!
Time is short.
Moi, je veille au de -
I will watch at the
Adagio.
pp
Me
hors!
door!
Faust.
Andante.
Recit.
Mon
My
Fl., Ob., & Cl.
p
coeur est pé - né - tré d'é - pou - van - te!
heart is o - ver - come with com - pas - sion!
Ob., Cl., Bn.
f
dim.
p

Ô tor - tu - re! Ô sour - ce de re - grets et d'é - ter - nels re -
O what tor - ture! O foun - tain of re - gret and ev - er - last - ing re -
Moderato.
mords! C'est el - le, la voi - ci,
morse! I see her, she is here,
Ob.
la dou - ce cré - a - tu - re, Je - tée au fond d'u - ne pri -
That sweet and love - ly be - ing, Im - pris - oned in this dun - geon
Fl.
cresc.
son comme u - ne vi - le cri - mi - nel - le! Le désespoir
here, Like an - y crim - i - nal of - fend - er! And her de - spair
dim.
p
é - ga - ra sa rai - son! Son pauvre enfant,
has be - wil - dered her mind! And her poor child,
Clar.
cresc.

F.
ô Dieu! son pauvre enfant tu-é,— tu-é par el-le!
o God. Her wretch-ed child is dead,— Killed by its moth-er!
f
sf dim.
Vcl.
p
F.
Ma.
Mar-gue-ri-te! Mar-gue-ri-te!
Mar-ga-ri-ta! Mar-ga-ri-ta!
(waking)
Margarita.
Recit.
Ah! c'est la voix du bien-ai-mé!— A son ap-pel mon cœur c'est ra-ni-mé!
Ah! That is my be-lov-ed's voice!— Hear-ing him call, my heart wak-ens a-gain!
Faust.
Mar-gue-ri-te!
Mar-ga-ri-ta!
Vlns.
pp
Margarita.
Au mi-lieu de vos é-clats de ri-re, Dé-mons qui m'en-tou-
Sweet and clear, o-ver your bursts of laugh-ter, You de-mons ev-er

rez, j'ai re-con-nu sa voix! Sa
near, I re-cog-nize his voice! And
Faust.
Mar-gue-ri-te!
Mar-ga-ri-ta!
cresc.
main, sa dou-ce main m'at-ti-re! Je suis li-bre! il est
now I feel his pres-ence near me! He will free me! He has
f
là! je suis li-bre, il est là, je l'en-tends, je le
come! I am free, he is here, I have heard his dear
Allegro non troppo.
vois! Oui, c'est toi, je t'ai-me, oui, c'est toi, je
voice! Yes, my sweet be-lov-ed, Yes, it's you, I
Vlns.
f
dim.
p

cresc.
dim.
Ma.
t'ai - me, Les fers, la mort mê - me Ne me font plus
love you, Now death can - not ev - er fright - en me a -
cresc.
dim.
peur! Tu m'as re - trou - vé - e,
gain. Once more you have found me,
p
Vcl.
tu m'as re - trou - vé - e, Me voi - là sau -
Once more you have found me. You have come to
cresc.
dim.
vé - e, me voi - là sau - vé - e! C'est toi, je suis
save me, You have come to save me. At last I am
cresc.
dim.
pp
— sur ton coeur!
— in your arms!
Faust.
F.
Oui, — c'est moi, je t'ai - me, oui, c'est moi, je
Yes, — my sweet be - lov - ed, Yes, it's I, I
Vlns.
espress.

F.
dim.
t'ai - me, Mal-gré l'ef-fort mê - me Du dé-mon mo -
love you De - spite all en - deav - ors Of the e - vil
cresc.
dim.
queur, Je t'ai retrou-vé - e, je t'ai retrou -
fiend. Once more I have found you, Once more I have
Vcl.
cresc.
vé - e, Te voi-là sau - vé - - e,
found you. I have come to save you,
cresc.
dim.
Te voi-là sau-vé - e, C'est moi, viens, viens sur mon
I have come to save you. My love, come, come to my
dim.
pp

Tempo del Valzer.
(He attempts to take her away; she gently avoids his arms.)
Margarita (her mind wandering)
F. Ma.
cœur!
arms.
At - tends!
Ah, wait!
f
dim.
pp
Ma.
Voi - ci la ru - e
Do you re - mem - ber
ppp
Où tu m'as vu - e Pour la pre - miè - re fois,
There in the street Where you and I first met?
Où vo - tre main o - sa presque ef - fleu - rer mes
Where once your hand Pressed my own As you said to

Andantino.
doigts. «Ne permettrez-vous pas, ma bel-le de-moi-
me: "Will you per-mit me, pray, My fair and gra-cious
Vcl.
sel-le, Qu'on vous of-fre le bras pour fai-re le che-min?»
la-dy? May I give you my arm And es-cort on your way?"
«Non, mon-sieur, je ne suis de-moi-sel-le ni bel-le, de-moi-
"No, my lord, I am nei-ther a la-dy nor gra-cious, nei-ther
pp
poco rit.
sel-le ni bel-le, Et je n'ai pas be-soin qu'on me don-ne la
la-dy nor gra-cious, Nor do I need To be es-cort-ed on my
colla voce

a tempo
Ma.
main.»
way."
Faust.
F.
Oui, mon cœur se sou-vient... mais suis-moi, l'heu-re
Yes, I re-mem-ber it well! Come with me, we must
p a tempo
cresc.
Adagio.
F.
Ma.
Margarita.
pas - se...
has - ten!
Et voi-ci le jar-din char-
I re-mem-ber the gar-den,
Vlns.
f
Harp
pp
ppp
mant,
too,
Par-fu-mé de myrte et de ro-se, Où cha-que
Fra-grant with the sweet scent of ros-es, Where in the
soir dis-crè-te-ment Tu pé-né-trais à la nuit clo-
dark of gen-tle night We felt the joy of love en-close

se... Non! non!
us. No! No,
Faust.
Viens, viens, Mar-gue-ri-te, viens, viens, fu-yons!
Come, come, Mar-ga-ri-ta! Come, we must flee!
cresc.
pp
cresc.
dim.
non! reste en-co-re. O ciel!..
stay! I im-plore you! O God,
Faust.
El-le ne m'entend
she does not un-der-
pp
f
Allegro. (♩. = 100)
pas!
stand!
Mephistopheles.
A-ler-te! a-
A-way then, a-
pp
ler-te! ou vous ê-tes per-dus! Si vous tardez en-
way then, Or you both will be lost! If you do not o-

Me.
Ma.
Margarita.
cor, je ne m'en mê - le plus! Le dé -
bey, No long-er count on me. It's the
f
Ma.
mon... le dé - mon! le vois - tu? là... dans
fiend! It's the fiend! Do you see? There in the
fp
Ma.
l'om-bre... Fi-xant sur nous son œil de feu?
shad-ow, His fi - ery eyes are star - ing at me!
cresc.
Maestoso.
Tempo I.
Ma.
Que nous veut-il? chas-se-le du Saint - lieu!
What does he want? Drive the de - mon a - way!
f
f
dim.

Mephistopheles.
Quit-tons ce lieu som - bre, le jour est le -
Un-less we de - part now It will be too
pp
vé; De leur pied so - no - re J'en-tends nos che -
late, I can hear my hors - es Im - pa - tient-ly
vaux frap - per le pa - vé.
champ Out - side at the gate.
f
Viens, sau-vons-la! peut-être il en est temps en-
Come, let us flee! Per-haps we still have time to
p
cresc.
f
p cresc.

Margarita.
Ma.
Mon Dieu, pro - té - gez - moi! mon Dieu, je vous im - plo - re! An - ges
My God, pro - tect me now! My God, I do im - plore you! Gath - er
co - re!
save - her!
Faust.
F.
Viens!
Come!
Fu - yons! peut - être il en est temps en -
A - way! Per - haps we still have time to
f
p
cresc.
rit. infino al Moderato

Moderato maestoso.
purs, an - ges ra - di - eux, Por - tez mon
nigh, an - gels of love, Car - ry my
co - re!
save you!
Moderato maestoso
Harps
âme au sein des cieux! Dieu
soul to God a - bove! For -
jus - te, à toi je m'a - ban - don - - ne! Dieu
give me in Thy in - fin - ite mer - - cy! For -
bon, je suis à toi, par - don - - ne! An - ges
give, Al-might-y God, for - give me! Gath - er
purs, an - ges ra - di - eux, Por - tez mon
nigh, an - gels of love, Car - ry my
cresc.

Ma.
âme au sein des cieux! Anges
soul to God a - bove! Gath-er
F.
Faust.
Viens, suis - moi; je le veux!
Come, you must! Come with me!
f
Ma.
purs, an - ges ra - di - eux, Por - tez mon
nigh, an - gels of love, Car - ry my
p
cresc.
Ma.
âme au sein des cieux! Dieu
soul to God a - bove! O
Me.
Mephistopheles.
Hâtons-nous!
Come a way,
f
Vlns.
p
Ma.
juste, à toi je m'a - ban - don - ne! Dieu
hear me, kind and heav-en-ly fa - ther, Al-
F.
Faust.
Viens! suis - moi!
Come, ah, come!
Me.
Mephistopheles.
L'heu-re son - ne!
Day is dawn - ing!
cresc.

Ma.
juste, à toi je m'abandonne! je suis à
mighty, kind and heaven-ly father, Almighty
F.
viens! suis moi! suis-
Come, ah come! Come with
Me.
Déjà le jour enva-
I see a glow in the
Ma.
toi, Dieu bon, pardonne! Anges
God, O Lord, forgive me! Angel
F.
moi, viens, je le veux!
me! Come, come with me!
Me.
hit, envahit les cieux!
sky, in the morning sky!
molto
f riten.

M.
purs, an - ges ra - di - eux, Por - tez mon
hosts, all gath - er nigh, Car - ry my
F.
Viens! viens! quittons ces lieux, Dé - jà le
Come, come! Let us fly! I see a
Me.
Hâ - tons - nous, hâ - tons - nous de quit - ter ces lieux, Dé - jà le
Let us haste, let us haste, for the dawn - is nigh. I see a
8
Me.
âme au sein des cieux! Dieu
soul to God on high! Al
F.
jour en - va - hit les cieux!
glow in the morn - ing sky!
Me.
jour en - va - hit les cieux!
glow in the morn - ing sky!
8
Ma.
jus - te, à toi je m'a - ban - don - ne! Dieu
might - y, kind and heav - en - ly fath - er, O
F.
Viens! viens! c'est
Come! Come! My
Me.
Suis nos pas, suis nos pas,
We must go! We must go!
8

Ma.
bon, je suis à toi, par - don - ne! An - ges
Lord, Al-might-y God, for - give me! An - gel
F.
moi, c'est moi qui te l'or - don - ne!
love! My love! You must be - lieve me!
Me.
viens, ou je t'a - ban - don - ne!
Come, come! Or I must leave you!
8
Ma.
purs, an - ges ra - di - eux, Por - tez mon
hosts, all gath - er nigh, Car - ry my
F.
Viens! viens! quit - tons ces lieux, Dé - jà le
Come, come! Let us fly! I see a
Me.
Hâ - tons - nous, hâ - tons - nous de quit - ter ces lieux! Dé - jà le
Let us haste, let us haste, for the dawn is nigh! I see a
8
Ma.
ff
âme au sein des cieux.
soul to God on high!
F.
ff
jour en - va - hit les cieux!
glow, for the dawn is nigh!
Me.
ff
jour en - va - hit les cieux!
glow, for the dawn is nigh.
8
ff

Ma.
F.
Me.
Pour-quoi ce regard mena - çant?
But why do you threat-en me so?
Mar-gue-ri-te!
Mar-ga-ri-ta!
Drum
Pourquoi ces mains rouges de sang? va!
And why is blood stain-ing your hands? Go!
tu me fais hor-reur!
I can't bear the sight!
Ah!
Ah!
Mephistopheles.
Ju-gé-e!
Dam-na-tion!
f
ff
fff

Nº 19a. Apotheosis

ff
Christ est res-sus-ci-té!
Christ the re-deem-er lives!
ff
Christ est res-sus-ci-té!
Christ the re-deem-er lives!
ff
Christ est res-sus-ci-té!
Christ the re-deem-er lives!
8
ff (Organ)
(Orch.)
3
Vi =
Christ vient de re-naî-tre!
Te De-um lau-da-mus!
Paix et fé-li-ci-té
Peace and good will on earth!
(Organ)
(Orch.)
Aux dis-ci-ples du maî-tre!
Glo-ria in ex-cel-sis!
Christ vient de re
Christ rose un-to

End of the Opera.

Faust.
Ballet.

Allegretto, Mouvement de Valse.

p
cresc.
f
p
p
sempre p
p
p
p
p
p
p
cresc.

p
cresc.
molto
8
f
dim.
p
sempre p
Ped.

Adagio.
2.
p
Ped.
*
Ped.
*
Ped.
*
p ma con suono
cresc.
cresc.
p
cresc.
p
cresc.
p
p leggieramente.
p

f
dim.
p
f
dim.
p
cresc.
p
cresc.
cresc.
p
cresc.

p
cresc.
p
8
8
p
Ped.

Allegretto.
3.
p
cresc. molto
f
p
p

cresc. molto

p
cresc.
molto
ff
3

Moderato maestoso.
4.
f
p
cresc. molto

f
dim.
p
cresc.
molto
f
ff
Ped.
f

Moderato con moto.
5.
p
cresc. molto
f
Ped.
*
dim.

p
p
p
Ped.
Ped.
Ped.
Ped.
Ped.

dim.
p
Ped.
dim.
p
p
pp
Allegretto.
6.
ff
p

p
cresc.
f
p
Ped.
p
cresc.
f

p
p

p
6
f
Allegro vivo.
7.
2/4
ff

ff

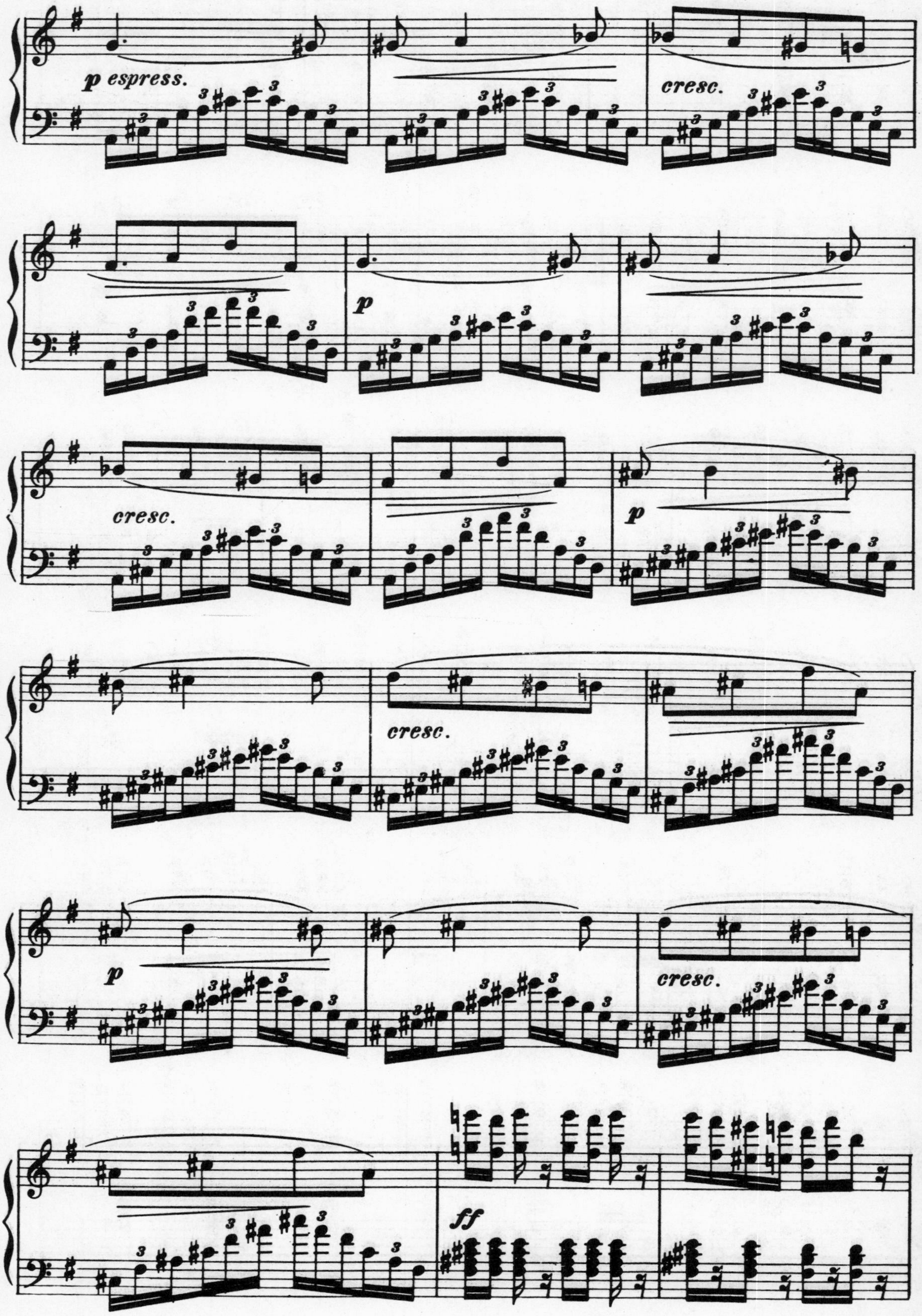
p espress.
cresc.
p
cresc.
p
cresc.
p
cresc.
ff

ff

p
dolce.
cresc.
p
cresc.

p
cresc.
molto
8
ff

più animato.
ff
Moderato.
8
Andantino.
8